G000255940

My Secret Affair with Chocolate Cake…

The Emotional Eater's Guide to Breaking Free

Sunita Pattani

J Publishing Company Ltd.
London

IMPORTANT

This book is not intended as a substitute for medical advice. The intent of this book is to provide general information with regard to the subject matter covered. If medical advice or any other expert advice is needed then the services of an appropriate medical professional should be sought.

Printed in Great Britain

My Secret Affair with Chocolate Cake…

Foreword

I didn't know exactly what to expect when Sunita Pattani approached me to write the foreword to this book and asked if she could send a partial manuscript along to help me make my decision. After reading MY SECRET AFFAIR WITH CHOCOLATE CAKE, I felt I'd found a kindred spirit in its author. We'd both overcome decades long eating problems and were on a mission to spread the word through writing and counseling troubled eaters that it's within your grasp to make peace with food and your body. I wish there had been more books like this around when I was in the thick of my eating struggles half a lifetime ago, a guide that gently would have taken me by the hand and said, "You can do this. I did it and I'm going to teach you how to find your own way. It's alright. Just come along."

In the same way that we crave food, we are desperate for others to tell us how to have a "normal" relationship with it, exactly what we must do to heal. Wise, however, is the author like Sunita who refuses to give in to championing the external quick-fix, and instead treats you like the adult you are who has choices and who will learn to make the right ones for herself over time through self-reflection, encouragement, and practice.

As a professional who has 30-plus years in the field of eating disorders, I know that Sunita's guidelines to breaking free of emotional eating are effective—and refreshing. She encourages you to look at troubled eating not as a food problem alone, but as part of a dysfunctional relationship with yourself and the world at large. She teaches you how to be whole—actually, to return to your natural state of wholeness—by connecting the dots between your emotional and physical self, between your hungers for food and desire for other life pleasures, by attaching the parts of you that are estranged.

The message she is giving here is the one she has learned and lives by: trust yourself to know what you need from this book, from food, from life. MY SECRET AFFAIR WITH CHOCOLATE CAKE is so replete with information, exercises, insights, and examples that you likely will have to read it more than once to benefit from all its wisdom. It will teach you how to: change not only your behaviors but your beliefs; connect or reconnect to appetite signals about hunger and fullness; identify and experience emotions which you've been eating over; put food in its rightful place in your life; discover a peaceful, joyful and centered part of yourself that wants to nurture and love you and won't allow you to abuse food; experiment with ways to interact with food so that you will learn, once and for all, what works for you; view your appetite as a gift; turn off the negative chatter in your mind that puts you down and pulls you backward and turn on the tender encouragement which fills you with pride and propels you forward; slow down and accept change as a natural process that has its own pace and form; non-judgmentally observe what you feel, think, and do so that you're not eating—or living—in a fog of past or future, but are smack, dab in the present right where you belong.

In MY SECRET AFFAIR WITH CHOCOLATE CAKE, you'll find passages from Sunita's journey from troubled to "normal" eater, exercises and worksheets to help you explore and change your eating patterns, snippets from research studies which bolster the concept of intuitive eating, advice, suggestions and tips for creating the positive relationship with food you've always wanted, and a personal guide to enjoying food in a new way, one that doesn't run—or ruin—your life.

Karen R. Koenig, LCSW, M.Ed., February 4, 2012
Author of:
THE RULES OF NORMAL EATING
THE FOOD AND FEELINGS WORKBOOK
NICE GIRLS FINISH FAT
WHAT EVERY THERAPIST NEEDS TO KNOW ABOUT TREATING EATING AND WEIGHT ISSUES

"The shoe that fits one person pinches another; there is no recipe for living that suits all cases"

- Dr. Carl Gustav Jung

Book Dedications

For my Soul Mate: Hinal Pattani;
your support throughout the whole process has been amazing – this would not
have been possible without you!

For my Mum: Kanwaljit K Bhogal;
the best Mum in the world.

For my Dad: Jaswant Singh Bhogal;
who taught me the true meaning of strength and perseverance – he is without
doubt the strongest person that I have ever met!

For my Mother-in-law: Indu Pattani;
for being understanding!

For my Soul Sister: Nisha Pattani,
the most amazing sister - and support network that anyone could ever ask for!

Acknowledgements

I would like to thank:

The Almighty Creator.

All my family who saw in me what I couldn't always see in myself.

Smita Rajesh for her support through this whole process.

Karen Koenig for taking time out of her busy schedule to review my manuscript and writing the foreword.

J Publishing for giving me the opportunity to get my work out there.

My mastermind group – you guys are amazing!

MY JOURNEY

A day in 2008 – (the date is irrelevant.... most of this happens every day).

I wake up. There it is again. The same feeling that I get most mornings. It's a 'binge-hangover'. I feel ill. I have a sickish feeling inside. I am starving, but unable to face food. I walk into the bathroom, silently having the same conversation with myself that I do each morning. Today is going to be different. Today is the start of a 'new me'. In six months, I'll be at my target weight. I can do this – all I have to do is to be disciplined about what I eat.

I look in the mirror. My face is bloated and I look tired. I *am* tired. After all, I have spent most of the night unable to sleep because the night before I had simply eaten to the point of being sick – again. It's a good thing that I have a phobia of being sick, otherwise I'd be bulimic by now. I reassure myself that everything is fine; if I can just stick to a diet I'll be fine. This has to work...

I don't understand why these episodes are so frequent. I mean I've binged ever since I can remember, but over the last five years it's got progressively worse. I want to stop more than anything else in the whole world, but it's like a demon awakens inside me each day. I go into a trance. I lose control.

I don't care.

I eat.

And eat. And eat. And eat.

Everyday it's the same pattern. I am brushing my teeth and feel that same anxious feeling. How long will it be before my husband leaves me? Why don't people understand what I am going through? I can't go out because I don't have any nice clothes that fit. I can't go out being this size. What will people think? My whole family thinks I am anti-social. How can I make them understand that I love going out, but I just can't? How many more social gatherings can I put off?

My worst fear is that someone really close to me will die, and I'll have to attend their funeral looking like this. How selfish can I be?

I have been good all morning. Then it starts. This uncontrollable urge for food takes over. I have to eat. *Oh my gosh Sunita, you just did it again. You're disgusting. Why can't you stop this and get a grip? Look at you. You're huge, and getting bigger each day.*

Evening comes and the eating continues. Bedtime comes and the eating continues. *I can't eat another mouthful or I'll throw-up everywhere.* I get ready for bed. My husband asks me how my day has been today with food. I tell him it's been fine. I tell him he won't have to wait long; I'll be in shape soon. I'll start going to all his shows again. We'll start socialising. *Good.* I smile. *I just lied again.*

Today

I am a lot more relaxed about food and eating.

I spent most of the first twenty-eight years of my life wishing I was someone else. I was desperate to get rid of the constant cycle of bingeing and starving. I hated my body. Why couldn't I have been born a 'thin person'? *Why did I have to work so hard at maintaining my weight*? I didn't realise that this very attitude, these very feelings were a significant contributor in keeping me trapped in a cycle of binge eating. The food had somehow become a coping mechanism and a substitute for the love that I was unable to show myself.

Then one day when the pain became unbearable, I decided that I had to change - either that, or live the rest of life in my house, completely isolated, friendless, family-less, loveless, and eventually lifeless.

Without doubt, it was the most frightening decision that I have ever made in my life. There was only one problem: I couldn't bear the thought of going on another diet. I had already been on numerous diets and knew that they only led to short-term success. I just couldn't put myself through the torture of counting anymore points, syns, calories, (*or whatever else*)... and of course attending those dreaded weekly weigh-ins. You know the sort I am talking about - the ones where you don't eat for four hours beforehand, pee a million times before you get there, and then finally, strip to bare minimum when you do get there. (Taking into account of course, that the choice of clothing must be the appropriate - after all we wouldn't want those jeans to add on that extra half-a-pound now would we?)

And then, after all that (*as if we haven't put ourselves through enough already*), have the class leader give you 'that look'...The one where she silently says, "*how dare you gain half a pound.*" Of course, at this point, if looks could kill, you'd be gone!

Although I had read some books centred around the idea of losing weight without dieting, I still wasn't sure what to expect. In the past I had to be either starving myself, on a diet or bingeing. What frightened me most was that I didn't know any other way to eat. I was afraid that if I gave myself permission to eat what I wanted without any structure, I would continue to get bigger, but I was stuck in such a horrible place that this was the only option left for me. Eventually, I told myself that surely I wouldn't want to eat all day (bearing in mind that's what I had been doing up until now), and if I didn't eat all day long, then the weight had to come off. Was I sure? No, but there was no other way.

And so my journey began. It was tough, I stumbled a lot. It took me a while to adjust to the new ideas, and sometimes, without realising, I would still try to control what I was eating. Other times, I would have binges that lasted four weeks. There were some shocking revelations too - one of which was that I actually suffered from Premenstrual Syndrome! You see, because my bingeing had been quite prevalent throughout all my life, I could never tell whether I was hungrier at certain times during the month. Also, because I was eating a lot of the time, I hardly ever craved any foods. I honestly thought I was one of those lucky girls who had managed to escape PMS symptoms. When I started to improve my relationship with food, I realised that I did get hungrier on certain days. In the beginning I found this very difficult to cope with, I couldn't understand what was happening. I thought that if I let myself eat when I was hungry, I would put on weight. It took a lot of 'trusting myself', and chance taking to discover that this was not the case. Despite all of this going on, bingeing episodes and all, I still managed to lose weight and improve my relationship with food. I noticed how resilient my body actually was.

After a while, I realised that I could help other people by sharing my experience and strategies with them, and so **My Secret Affair with Chocolate Cake** was born. I started working with clients and watched with joy as they started to heal their relationship with food and unlock their natural body weight.

However, there was one issue which just kept on niggling away at me inside. Although a majority of my clients were making phenomenal progress, it became apparent to me after a while that there were a few people who were finding it really difficult to implement this approach. What was even more frustrating was that, as time went by I too would occasionally revert back to my old habits again and binge like there was no tomorrow. I was puzzled. I couldn't understand how all these people were making progress around me after engaging in *my work*, whilst I and a few others were sometimes encountering enormous difficulty.

I started to re-research the work which I knew was similar to mine in order to try and find a missing link, but didn't find what I was looking for. (Well, I did eventually, but not where I was looking. I will share this with you in the next chapter.) Some of the approaches were too rigid – this went against the very nature of my work which encourages people to eat whatever they want (within the boundaries of hunger and satiety). I knew deep within that the body will guide you if you let it.

But, I did find something interesting. Whilst doing some research on how other people had responded to work similar to mine, I found that although many people had benefitted greatly, there were a few that had reported that their overeating had become worse as a result of allowing themselves permission to eat whatever they wanted. What was even more astonishing was that some people had actually gained weight as opposed to losing it. It was at that point that something within me clicked - not all emotional eaters were the same. Emotional eaters came in varying degrees, but there were some people who literally felt completely out of control around food and no matter what they did, they still felt compelled to eat. There was something very familiar about this finding – it was exactly what I had experienced.

I started to toy around with the idea that perhaps certain foods had a particular physiological effect on some people, which left them craving for more of a particular food and, upon doing some research, I found some studies that suggested that excessive sugar intake may function in similar ways to addictive substances[1]. Did this mean that I and a number of my clients were food addicts? Perhaps, I wasn't sure. But what I was sure of was this: when someone can't get through their day without continually obsessing about food; when someone can't stop eating; when their marriage is on the brink of a break-up because they refuse to go out of the house; when they buy and eat food in secret, or wait for others to leave the house before they eat; when they want to stop this pain more than anything else and they can't, something is terribly wrong.

The principles outlined in this book will work for anyone if they focus on

---

1 Boscarsly, M. (2009) Sugar Addiction, More than Just a Sweet Tooth? Food Ethics Summer 2009, Vol.4, issue 2 www.foodethicscouncil.org

them. However, if you do find yourself in a place where you go through phases of feeling out of control around food, then you may have to put some additional strategies (which have also been suggested in this book) in place to help you along the way.

Using this book

I have come to realise that for many people, making peace with food can be a complex process. And whilst there will be some of you that will find it extremely easy to take the information from this book and apply it, others of you will find that it will open the doors up to discovering more about who you really are. What I have found to be true is that the way in which we eat is a direct reflection of the way in which we live our lives. Our relationship with food tells us more about ourselves than what we realise, and although many of us wonder why we have to go through this constant battle with weight and food, we fail to realise that if we could just find the strength to take a brief look into the misery that we are experiencing, we may just find the answers to our questions.

I have found that establishing a healthy relationship with food is a multi-layered process. There are many reasons and opinions for why some people have an unhealthy relationship with food. Some believe that the issue can be tackled solely by a change in diet and exercise, whilst others believe that the issue is one of a psychological nature. And whilst I don't disagree entirely with these opinions, having been through a very turbulent relationship with food, I personally believe that taking a close look at an individual as a 'whole', (which includes mind, body and soul) needs to be considered and addressed in order to initiate a permanent change in one's relationship with food.

I believe that each of us is born with some inherent knowledge. I feel we possess some invaluable tools which, if nurtured properly, will guide us how to live life. Have you ever noticed how babies only eat when they want to, stop when they've eaten enough, possess the amazing quality of forgiveness , never seem to give up - even if they fall a hundred times before taking their first step, find joy in the smallest of things and know how to dream big? It's true! We are all born with a desire to live life to its fullest, and yet for most of us, something somewhere goes drastically wrong.

John Welwood, author of *Love and Awakening*[2] uses a wonderful analogy to describe our inner world. Imagine being a huge castle with many beautiful but different rooms, each one with its own character, adding a different shade to make you 'whole'. Some rooms will shine brightly because the windows are grand and the sun sharp, whereas others enjoy the influence of the shade. We love exploring our castle because it's exciting, and it doesn't matter that the rooms are decorated differently because we know that each one can be appreciated in a different way. Then one day a family member or a friend visits and tells us that the darker room is not pleasing to the eye, and really has no use. "Why don't you just close it off?" they say, "Nobody is going to like to come and stay in that room." You feel a little disheartened that they don't like your room, because you have had many wonderful experiences in there. But keen to please, and with a slight hesitance, you close the door and lock it off. Month by month, year by year, you receive more visitors, each with their own view on your beautiful castle, some do not like the size of the rooms and others the colour, and as each one leaves, another door closes. Before your very eyes, your castle grows smaller and smaller and you begin to experience a loss of freedom. Before long you can't even remember what some of the rooms look like. You're no longer a castle, but instead you've become a small apartment needing some major refurbishment works. But you tell yourself that it doesn't matter, everyone does this. And at least you're liked.

There's something about this analogy that, when shared with others, seems to strike a chord. At some level deep down, this message resonates with people, bringing to their attention a 'knowing' that there is an element of truth to what they have just heard. Why? **Because we all have a natural desire to flourish, to live life joyfully and to experience wonder**. At some point in our lives, someone has come along and advised us to close the door on ourselves. Their well-meaning intentions and messages have sometimes left us feeling that somehow we are not good enough, worthy enough, intelligent enough, healthy enough or thin enough. The fact that we learn to close the doors on our body, believing that a thinner form will bring us greater happiness is a considerable illusion, but even greater is the illusion that we cannot be trusted to feed ourselves appropriately, that someone or something outside of us knows us better than we do.

The reason that food restriction alone does not help a majority of people is because it doesn't teach us how to open up that closed door. Therefore we are not working in harmony with our natural instincts. Instead, we choose to live under a misconception that manages to persuade us that if we can just stick to this new diet for twelve weeks, we will achieve that perfect body that we have so been longing for. This is false. I know it's false because I've been on many diets, I've reasoned with the process a thousand times over, I've told myself time and time again that this was it – this new diet was going to deliver its promise to me, if I could just be disciplined enough to stick with it.

It took me a long time to decide on the order of the chapters within this book. After starting my journey, I soon realised that moving towards a healthier relationship with food was not about following rules, but more about trusting in yourself and listening to your body. I also felt that having knowledge about the way in which your mind works was essential, because it gave you an understanding of why you developed the food challenge in the first place. Therefore this book presents a number of chapters, incorporating a range of topics designed to help you re-establish a healthy relationship with food.

In order to obtain the maximum benefit from this book, I strongly urge you to read the whole book through at least once because this book is a process. Although many of you may easily achieve success by just incorporating the physical principles, for some of you, the emotional component will be invaluable – not just for the purpose of attaining your natural body shape, but also in helping you in every area of your life. It is probably a little different to what you may have read before, but will tie together properly once you reach the end.

So here's to your success! I hope this journey is going to be as enlightening for you as it has been for me. Welcome to freedom!

I AM JOY

My natural state is one of well-being

I am whole, a composite of mind, body and life

I deserve to realign with my natural body shape

I deserve to feel the magnificence that I am. I am connected and yet appreciate my individuality

I appreciate my skills

I take pride and joy in all that I do

I look for the joy in all aspects of my life

Joy is the remedy that will fill the emotional void

I AM JOY

1

WHERE ARE YOU?

"A good starting point is knowing where you are"

- Sunita Pattani

There is always a reason why people overeat. Whether it stems from physiological reasons, emotional reasons, or just unconsciousness, there is a reason. I think it's rare that any two people will ever share the exact same experience. Each one of our experiences is different. Unique. But we are all human, and although it may not always be apparent to us, we fail to realise that we all deal with things in the same way. No matter what the outward manifestation may be, whether it's binge eating, smoking, alcohol or drug abuse, it's a signal. It's a signal telling us that there is something wrong and that we need to become more aware of who we are and what we really need.

What is Emotional Eating?

When I was young, at some point I heard a relative say, "I am an emotional eater. Every time things get really bad, I sneak into the bathroom with my favourite packet of biscuits and eat them." For a long while, I believed that all emotional eaters ate like this and I also remember thinking that I couldn't possibly be an emotional eater. For a start, I never ate in the toilet and secondly, I didn't like biscuits much. *Nope, not me. Emotional eating is what other people did, older people. People with real problems in their life. Emotional eating...I mean, what was it anyway?*

It took me a long while to realise that emotional eating came in many different forms and sizes. Even people who have a healthy relationship with food may eat emotionally on rare occasions. My personal definition for emotional eating is *when an individual eats in response to feelings instead of hunger*. I actually think that there are a lot of people who eat emotionally and just don't realise it. Quite often the weight that they gain is an outcome of the way that they eat and food choices that they make. And although at this point it may not be obvious, but even the choice of food tells you about the way that you are feeling and what you really want.

Now, you already know my reasons for writing this book, but before I share the tools with you, I want to share with you three factors that will form the foundation of realigning with your natural body weight.

The Foundation

1. **We need to look at ourselves as being 'whole'.**

   If realigning with our natural body weight was all just about the body, then sticking to a diet and losing the weight would be a fairly straight forward process, because the theory makes sense: control your eating and you'll lose the weight. But, both our experience and results have shown us that this is not the case.

   I don't believe that you are just a body alone. I believe that you are a composite of three elements: body, mind and soul, and all three of these elements need to work in harmony with one another to achieve the desired result. Your soul is your life force. Your mind is responsible for your thoughts, emotions and actions, and your body is a physical manifestation of your thoughts – a vehicle through which you experience life.

   Treating the body alone is only tackling part of the issue. In addition to being aware of your hunger and satiety levels, I also believe that you have to be aware of the nature of your natural state (which is one of well-being), as well as the way in which your mind works in order to implement a long lasting change.

2. **Our natural state is one of well-being**

   We live on a planet that is amazingly designed to perfection. There is a constant supply of air for us to breathe; there is an abundant supply of water, which is part of the well thought-out cycle of evaporation; the weather changes to accommodate our different needs; and the Earth provides us with digestible nutrition.

   Do you honestly believe that we human-beings are anything but perfect? Think about it for a moment: we are so intelligently designed that our bodies actually strive to heal a cut as soon as we hurt ourselves. We are perfection. We are built in such a way that our natural body systems point towards well-being all the time, but yet we fail to realise it. We spend so much time looking at what we don't want instead of the amazing miracles that we already are, that we sometimes miss the point altogether. Well-being is our birth right and our natural body weight is already hard-wired within us and becomes accessible once we accept this realisation. I haven't yet met a single person who has achieved a long lasting change by hating themselves. Those who achieve a long lasting change recognise who they really are and how much power lies within them.

3. **Our need to eat when we're not hungry is a calling that we need to find out what is really going on within us.**

One of my clients, Jo, had tried everything to lose weight and make peace with food. She told me that her latest attempt involved replacing eating with another activity. In other words, when she felt a craving she would take a walk or phone a friend. But after giving it a go, she found it wasn't working. She was feeling so disheartened that she feared that she would never be able to make peace with food or realign with her natural body weight.

Jo wasn't the only client who faced this hurdle. Do you remember in the last chapter I mentioned how it puzzled me that some of my clients would make amazing progress and others (including myself) would sometimes struggle? There seemed to be a missing link.

Well, after much research I found an answer. I already knew that when we ate, it was to fill a void, but then I would get stuck. I didn't completely understand what that void was, or how else to fill it. After some research and continual personal practice, it came to light that at the core of emotional eating lies our inability to really connect with ourselves - to feel what we're really feeling. This can manifest as a constant subtle feeling of discomfort, that we don't even realise is there, and it is this underlying feeling that we respond to when we eat emotionally.

When we eat for reasons other than hunger, we eat to provide ourselves with something. Whether that something is comfort, numbness, excitement, sweetness, or a feeling of stability, we're using food to fill a void that really needs to be felt and acknowledged. The way to freedom with food is to experience the feelings within. The mind may tell you lies, but your body is the epitome of truth. It tells all. And if you let it, it will guide you to freedom.

So ultimately, it doesn't matter what action you try to take to fix your eating habits or your weight, if you don't work on your thoughts and feelings, and if you don't commit to really getting to know yourself, you're unlikely to make long term progress. This is why replacing her eating with an activity didn't work for Jo, because she wasn't tackling the core issue. In order to re-establish a healthy relationship with food, and in order to realign with your natural body weight, you first need to get a better understanding of yourself.

What sort of an eater are you?

Now that you are aware of the foundation, the next step is to become more aware of the sort of eater that you are. I have listed below some of the most common reasons why people turn to food, and from experience I have found that most of my clients fit into one or more of these categories. Please note that if you do identify with any of these factors, the idea is not to dwell on this discovery, but more to use it as a tool of awareness to help you recognise old patterns if they try to crop up. This will be covered in more detail throughout the book.

1.   **Eating to numb emotions**

     This has probably stemmed from childhood where you were given food to help you numb a particular discomfort. For example, you may have been given a cookie if you fell over and started to cry and this habit has simply continued. You now find yourself reaching for food when anything uncomfortable happens. The thing to remember however, is that in reality the food only numbs your emotions whilst you are actually eating the food. It is a temporary fix. Once you have finished eating, the uncomfortable emotion may come back, along with the added guilt of the food that you have just consumed.

2.   **Eating can be a way of showing yourself some love**

     At some level, many of us have forgotten our own magnificence and who we really are. As we are growing up, we quickly learn the difference between acceptable and non-acceptable behaviour, so we try to hide away the parts of ourselves that we are ashamed of. Rather than acknowledging that we are a 'whole' person capable of displaying all types of behaviour, and that we are worthy of love, a part of us begins to believe that we are unworthy and unlovable. And because there is a part of us that feels this, we are unable to provide ourselves with the love that we need, and hence we use food as a substitute. The fact of the matter is that there is the same life force that runs through us, as does through any other person. We are just as worthy, capable and lovable as our greatest idol. If we could truly recognise our own magnificence, we would no longer require the extra food as love. We would understand that we are Love.

3.   Eating may symbolise fear

I know that this may sound strange, but people are fearful of a lot of things. I have had clients who:

- Are fearful of attracting the opposite sex.

- Fear that if they become slim, they will somehow become 'un-healthy' - for some people (and sometimes some cultures), this is because they have an association of weight symbolising health.

- Continue to eat because they fear that they may lose their friends if they lose weight.

- Are so accustomed to being on a diet, or yo-yo dieting, that they fear what they will do once they lose the weight. It's almost as if they will have nothing else left to aim for.

I would also like to point out that it may be possible that certain family members are encouraging you to eat due to their own fears. It isn't unheard of, for example, for a husband to encourage his wife to continue eating, as he may be scared of her attracting male attention.

4.   Eating due to boredom or as a means of rewarding yourself

It's very common for children to be given food to reward them for a particular activity, such as cleaning their room. The only issue however, is that they continue this pattern into adulthood. I often come across clients who reward themselves with food if they happen to lose a bit of weight. This is especially common amongst individuals who attend regular weekly weigh-in meetings, who come back home and really pile a plate high full of 'free foods' and some extra 'forbidden goodies' – knowing that they have the whole week to put things right again.

Not all emotional eaters are the same

Harry's Story

From as far back as he could remember, Harry had always been overweight. He'd tried some diets but had been unsuccessful; he had almost come to the conclusion that he would always be overweight. Harry has generally had a happy life and has a good career. He doesn't have any major challenges, but feels that his weight has always held him back from achieving his maximum potential.

When Harry was introduced to My Secret Affair with Chocolate Cake, he felt that he had been given the tools to set him free. Although he still overate on some occasions, he felt much more at ease with himself and the choices of food that he was making. He found that one of the biggest factors that held him back was the fact that he had previously denied himself certain foods, which on the odd occasion when he decided to consume these, resulted in him eating them uncontrollably.

Ever since Harry has started listening carefully to his hunger-satiety signals, and allowed himself to eat whatever his body wants, the desire to eat 'crazily' has subsided. He is very relaxed around food nowadays and has dropped 42lbs in six months. After realising that he really wants to live and enjoy life, Harry has recently joined the gym – not to lose weight, but to feel good.

Simone's Story

Although she wasn't overweight as a teenager, Simone has always felt fat. As the years have gone by, she has tried virtually every diet under the sun and has consistently gained weight. Simone was more desperate to lose the weight than she was to make peace with food. She feared that if she couldn't get to an 'acceptable' size, then she would never really enjoy life properly. In the recent years, Simone's struggle had become harder and she battled with herself each day, hoping that she would be able to lose the weight quickly.

When Simone started My Secret Affair with Chocolate Cake, she wasn't sure what to expect. She found eating whatever she wanted very difficult as she didn't trust herself around food. She found that surrounding herself with her favourite foods just didn't work as she ended up eating them.

However, over time she realised that certain foods weren't nourishing her body, but were instead a call from the mind. She learned how to watch for her emotions and care for herself in other ways. But more importantly, she made an amazing discovery: as she began to accept where she was, and as she started to live and have a good time regardless of her weight, she noticed that her weight started to normalise. Simone lost 28lbs over a period of 2 years and now has a healthy relationship with food.

It's important to realise that not all emotional eaters are the same. Some people experience mild levels of emotional eating, whereas other people would describe themselves as 'food addicts'. The thing to remember is that this is your journey, and for various reasons, including your physiological, psychological and genetic make-up, you will experience it differently from any other person.

Harry and Simone are both real life examples of people that I have worked with. Having worked with a range of clientele, I have come to realise that although ultimately everyone has to correct their underlying feelings about themselves and their relationship to life, their approach may be very different. Although displaying low self-esteem, Harry had two main issues. Firstly, he had been so accustomed to overeating that he didn't realise that he already had a natural hunger-fullness signal system, and hence always consumed more food than his body required. Secondly, he realised very quickly that 'food deprivation' (which had been brought about by the few diets that he had tried), was a major reason why he over indulged.

Once Harry understood the way that his body and mind worked, he found it fairly easy to implement the principles outlined in this book. He took the step to allow himself to eat 'forbidden foods' whenever his body called for them, and after a short while, the food lost its power over him, which helped him to realign with his natural body weight fairly quickly.

Simone on the other hand was a different case altogether. She had many challenges which were intertwined. As she learned more about her body, she realised that she had to make a conscious choice to be mindful of her sugar intake as she always felt compelled to consume more of it. She understood that this wasn't a 'rule', but a choice that **she had eventually chosen to make** because she wanted to live, feel good and respect herself.

The point is that the principles outlined in this book will work for anyone, but you have got be willing to become an expert on you. The more you commit to learning about yourself and the more you begin to question the reasons for your overindulgences, the more fulfilling the journey will become.

So now that you have an idea of why you eat the way you do, let's explore the world of dieting…

I AM TRUTH

I know that I have the power to unlock my natural body shape

The answer lies within me

My body knows its truth and if I listen carefully enough and respect myself, my body will guide me

The truth of what is good for me is always revealed before my eyes

Truth is something that I am always connected to

My body is truth

I speak my truth

I AM TRUTH

2

THE TRUTH ABOUT DIETING

*"If Einstein defined insanity as doing the same thing over and over again and expecting different results, then I must be the **insanest** person on Earth!"*

- Sunita Pattani

The Issue with Dieting

To say that diets don't work would be inaccurate. For some people, diets do help to shift the weight. The issue is not in whether diets work in removing the weight, but instead whether they are a long term solution to keeping the weight **off**.

It is interesting to note that in the UK obesity is on the rise. In 1993, 13% of men were considered to be obese along with 16% of women. In 2008, we saw an increase in these figures to 24% for men and 25% for women[3]. Furthermore in 2006, the Department for Health forecasted that by 2010, 6.6 million men and 6 million women would be obese in the UK if trends continued.

Dieting is not the solution to the obesity epidemic, we only need to look at the long-term results that the diet industry is producing to realise that this is the case. Let's take a closer look at the world of diets:

1. Dieting only addresses the symptom.

Looking at it logically, dieting does represent a solution to a problem. A well balanced diet seems like a sensible approach to losing weight. There is however one issue: we are not entirely logical beings, we have an emotional side too, which has the capability of exerting a very strong pull over us. If this were not the case, following a diet and keeping the weight off long term would be easy. But we're not machines. We are walking, talking people with feelings and emotion, which means that the rigidity that dieting brings can be difficult to deal with in the long term. Food itself is not the issue. It's what's causing you to turn to the food that is the real issue. What is it that propels you to eat in the first place?

Let's take a look at what typically happens: The reality of the situation is that there is something within you (of which you may not be aware), that is propelling you to eat. After a while, the outcome is undeniable – weight gain. To further complicate the situation, the weight brings with it a whole array of new challenges: aching joints, high blood-pressure, the embarrassment of not being able to sit comfortably in an aeroplane, shortness of breath, guilt, worthlessness, and the list goes on...

Then we look at the obvious health and emotional manifestations and attempt to control these by lowering our weight, which is encouraged through a change in diet[4]. Whilst this seems like the right thing to do, it hardly ever works in the long run because we have missed the point altogether – we are aiming to fix something that isn't the real issue. It's like attempting to change the batteries in a toy when the actual mechanics of the toy need fixing. We can put the best quality of battery in there, but they will not be able to function long term, unless the inner mechanics are sorted out first.

2.   **Eventually dieting will chip away at your self-esteem**

Many of the people that have attended my workshops or had personal sessions with me started their first diet in their teens, and although at first it seemed like an easy, innocent approach, eventually it did chip away at their self-esteem. For most people, going on a diet is a bit like getting on a merry-go-round that picks up speed over time.

---

4 The ironic thing about this journey and our healing is that the overall issue is not about the food or the weight. But, once we reach a stage where we are experiencing physical and emotional challenges, then yes, it does become about the weight too, because the weight is now stopping us from experiencing life to its fullest.

The Diet Cycle

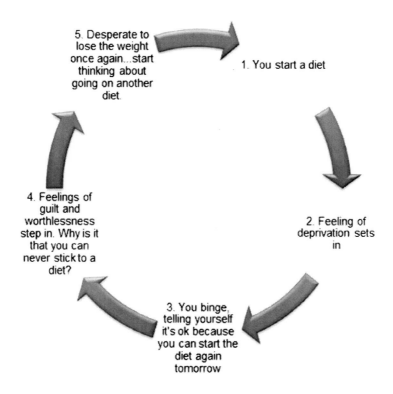

The important thing to realise is that every time we repeat this cycle, two things occur. Firstly, we may gain more weight. And secondly, the more we fail at any diet, the more we begin to feel that there's something wrong with us as individuals. We somehow manage to convince ourselves that we are the ones that lack the discipline required, that we are the ones who are not good enough, not strong enough, not in control because we can't even manage to mould ourselves into our preferred shape. As human beings we each have a desire to live and to experience life. We have an inherent yearning for joy and pleasure. The awkwardness that we feel about ourselves teamed up with rigid rules on what and how much to eat, simply doesn't work synonymously with the idea of joy and experiencing life to its fullest. In short, the overall result of dieting: a heavier you with a lower self-esteem.

3. **Everything within us and in our environment is going against us where dieting is concerned.**

As mentioned earlier, the real challenge that dieting presents is keeping the weight off in the long-term. When we choose to go on a diet, the only thing we consider is what do we have to do to lose the weight? We never stop to think about our environment and the effect it may be having on us.

There is academic research to support the anecdotal evidence of dieting. Wansink (2009) states that "*it is estimated that 95% of people who lose weight on a diet gain it back.*" He raises an interesting point saying that the reason why diets don't work is because they go against the very nature of our brains, bodies and environment. Diets, most of the time, involve some form of deprivation. However, our body doesn't respond well to any form of deprivation since we are biologically programmed with the instinct to eat. This also makes it very difficult to exercise willpower. The author also makes the points that we have millions of years of evolution and instinct telling us to eat as often, and as much as we can.

It's also worth considering the impact of our environment. The luring advertisements on television, the strategically planned supermarkets and the smells wafting through the shopping malls, all play a part in persuading us to eat. When I was 19 (and whilst being a member of a popular diet club), I went on holiday to Disney World in Florida. I remember planning in advance how, and what, I would be open to eating. However, when we arrived it was a different story, I found that I just couldn't stay away from the food - there was food everywhere! I actually remember feeling really miserable because I felt that I couldn't fully enjoy myself and constantly trying to keep myself in control around the food was exhausting. After about two days, I gave in. I ate. And ate. And ate. And ate.

Some years later, when I made a commitment to overcome my issues with food and eating, I started wondering about the effects that our environment was having on our eating patterns. I found that there had been a number of studies conducted that affirm the connection between our environment and the amount of food we consume.

The aim of one particular study cited in Wansink (2009) was conducted at the U.S. Army Research Labs in Massachusetts[5]. The aim of the study was to see whether troops could be encouraged to eat more when deployed in a combat situation. This was considered important as troops

---

5 Wansink, B. (2009) Mindless Eating – Why We Eat More Than We Think. Hay House Publishers, UK.

often burned up to 6000 calories a day and, therefore, keeping them well fuelled was essential. The main challenges faced by the researchers were the additional odours that the troops had to put up with, such as the smell of diesel, that often meant that their food tasted unappetising. The study involved a number of people eating oatmeal out of three different types of bowls: a normal bowl, a cinnamon-raisin odour infused bowl and a macaroni-and-cheese odour infused bowl. The results were interesting and showed that the people ate more from the cinnamon-raisin odour infused bowls, and ate a lot less from the macaroni-and-cheese odour infused bowls. What's interesting to note is that the taste of the actual oatmeal didn't change, but rather it was the different smells that had an influence on the amount eaten.

Marketers understand the connection between odours and cravings and label this "the Cinnabon Effect"[6] . Successful marketing is all about your memory and positive association with smell. The Cinnabon[7] stores understand this concept well and ensure that their stores are located next to other stores that don't sell food. This way, they encounter no "smell competition". You, as the customer would be doing just fine engaging in some much-needed retail therapy, and then you catch the Cinnabon goodness wafting through the air. That's it. You're hooked.

Taking this into consideration, it isn't surprising how well-intentioned diets may collapse and it certainly explained why my Disney World trip ended up turning into an "eat all I could" experience. Although the marketers had made their money from me, I was left feeling that I had "fallen off the wagon" and seeing as I was on holiday, I very quickly persuaded myself that I would start my diet again once I got back to the UK.... heavier.

4.	**The process of dieting may have a negative effect on the way in which you relate to food.**

There is evidence that suggests that dieting is not an effective method of weight loss in the long-tem. An article published in the American Psychologist (2007) reviewed a number of studies which looked at the long-term outcomes of a calorie restricted diet, and whether dieting is an effective treatment for obesity. The article concluded that the benefits of dieting

6 Wansink, B. (2009) Mindless Eating – Why We Eat More Than We Think. Hay House Publishers, UK.

7 An international franchise selling baked goodies and beverages.

were minimal, and the potential risks were too large for it to be recommended as a safe and effective treatment.

It should be noted that weight loss is not the only issue that is linked with dieting. In her book, *The Psychology of Eating*, Ogden discusses a few studies that show a link between dieting and mood. The first study highlighted was a study conducted in 1950. This study was based on a group of thirty-six non-dieting males who were subjected to a controlled diet for twelve weeks. During this period, they were only given approximately half their usual intake of food. The study found that these males developed negative changes in mood and concentration spans as well as a pre-occupation with food. After the study was complete and the participants once again resumed their usual eating habits, they reported episodes of binge eating as they lost control around food. It was concluded by the authors that these results may have come about due to the reduction of food that the participants experienced during the study. Warren & Cooper (1988) also obtained similar results when they invested the effects of dieting on seven men and seven women who were of normal weight. They concluded that although they found no significant changes in the mood of the participants, they did find that these participants had an increased preoccupation with thoughts about food.

These findings don't surprise me in the slightest. Most of the people that I have worked with have found that long-term dieting has caused them to become pre-occupied with thoughts of food. I have also had a few clients who have reported that the more that they dieted, not only did they think about food more, but they also consumed a lot more food too.

For example, Nancy started her first diet club at the age of 18, with the aim to release around 14lbs of weight. Although she reached her target weight, she struggled to keep it off and over the next twelve years engaged in cycles of strict diets and bingeing. At the age of 30, she was 42lbs heavier. She had started off with a relatively rational relationship with food, and couldn't understand how she had ended up so out of control.

5. **Take a close look at who diets are actually aimed at.**

A few weeks ago, a good friend of mine had been talking about my services to some of her friends, whom she knew wanted to lose weight. She told me afterwards that although she could see the need for some of her friends to engage in my services, she was shocked at how many of her "normal sized" friends were also eagerly stepping forward to find out about the workshops. She said that she couldn't understand why some of these women thought that they needed to lose weight, when they appeared to be of a "healthy size". I explained to her that it wasn't uncommon for me to come across this scenario, and that some of the women that I work with need to learn body acceptance more than anything else.

I am continuously amazed at the number of women that I see who (upon some reflection), remember being in a place where they were relatively happy with themselves, and then as a result of some small incident (perhaps an innocent comment from a well-meaning relative), triggered off the need for them to look or feel a different way. For many women, this becomes the start of an endless journey towards perfection. Some of the women manage to lose the weight and then are trapped in a continuous cycle to keep the weight off, whilst others find themselves losing the weight and then gaining it back, usually with a little extra each time, until they find themselves overweight and in despair. In fact, I remember being at my heaviest weight and looking through some old photographs of myself, wishing that I was that size again. The ironic thing however, is that even when I was that size - a size 10, I felt fat. I felt fat because some well-meaning people in my life from a very young age had planted the seed in mind that I was overweight, when really I was just a cute baby. As a result, it didn't matter how thin I tried to become, I still perceived myself as being "fat". Retrospectively, I can now say that stepping into the world of dieting worsened my situation because aside from some deprivation, it also silently taught me how to judge my self-worth by looking at a set of numbers on a scale.

This is why I feel that it's really important to closely consider who the dieting industry is supposed to be aimed at, and who *actually* engages in the services. It is worth noting that although diets may be considered as an avenue to tackle obesity, they are *available* to the whole of the public. In fact, some of the people who engage in dieting are neither obese, nor overweight and start the dieting journey as they feel that they have to look good, rather than the need to be healthy.

The thing is, although the dieting industry responds to a need by providing overweight individuals with support and relevant information, it also creates a need as well by working in three ways: First, it is part of the media world which supports the idealization of thinness, Second, it supports the idea that diets work, and third, it supports treating a perceived body size as an actual problem. If you look at the situation closely, it's a lucrative industry because it ensures that individuals continue to feel overweight and turn to dieting as a solution – a solution that clearly doesn't work in the long-term. It seems that that the dieting industry creates a need in order to fulfil the need, with a solution that has little chance of being successful. This notion of fulfilling a need is met due to the type of thinking that dieting creates. Many people who engage in dieting display classic 'black-and-white' thinking (discussed further in chapter 8), which may be translated as either "being on" a diet or "off a diet". Hence we may temporarily lose the ability to introduce balance both into our eating habits and our life.

6. **When we think about starting a dieting, we only think about the end result.**

It's true. When we start a diet we only consider the end result. But what happens in the space before we reach the end result, and after the end result has been achieved?

We often start diets under the illusion that that they will be a long-term solution and will bring us the happiness that we so desire, but this isn't the case. Yes, on a practical level, a slimmer body will probably make it easier to buy clothes and to physically get around. But, very rarely do we stop to think about what the long-term effects will be. It's not just about the food or about the weight; it's also about living life and enjoying the experiences that we encounter.

Think seriously for a moment, how depressing is it to know that you would have to be on a diet for the rest of your life in order to be slim? You would never have complete freedom. Even on occasions where you did 'treat' yourself, chances are you'd be too worried about eating too much of whatever you're measuring, that you probably wouldn't fully enjoy the food. You may also find yourself refusing to participate in social invitations for the fear that you may 'lose control' and gain weight as a result of having unlimited access to food. Where's the joy in that?

The truth is that many people miss out on the very experience of life because they are too busy either thinking or feeling fat, or obsessively worrying about what they're putting into their mouths. To make matters worse, many of my clients have said that in the past when they have been at their desired weight, they still felt unfulfilled. They somehow thought that a thinner body would lead to ultimate happiness, but they were wrong. Happiness is a state which is experienced from within and this can only be the case when we are somewhat comfortable and at peace with ourselves.

PUTTING IT INTO PRACTICE

The following activity has been designed to highlight your personal success with dieting so far. Although many of us know deep down that dieting is not the answer, sometimes a little self-reflection helps to make things clearer for us.

1. List all the diets that you have been on so far. (This includes any type of system where you have relied on an external source to dictate how and when you eat).

    ....
    ....
    ....
    ....
    ....
    ....
    ....

2. For how long did you engage in each diet and how much weight did you lose?

    ....
    ....
    ....
    ....
    ....
    ....
    ....

3. For each diet that you have listed in question 2, how long did you manage to keep the weight off for? Did you gain any additional weight back after the diet?

    ....
    ....
    ....

....
....
....
....

4. How did you feel whilst you were on the diet?

....
....
....
....
....
....
....

5. How much money do you think you've invested in total by engaging in dieting?

....
....
....
....
....
....
....

I AM BEAUTIFUL

I am beautiful inside-out

I enjoy the way that my body functions and I like being in good health

I like the fact that my body enables me to experience life

I consider it a miracle that my body is able to shift its shape

I appreciate the fact that my body can heal and sustain itself

I am able to shine my inner beauty and help to serve others

We are always in a place where we can experience limitless beauty because beauty is always in the eye of the beholder

I choose to see myself and others as beautiful

I AM BEAUTIFUL

3

ACCEPT YOUR NATURAL BODY SHAPE

"Just as a person with a shoe size of eight would not expect to realistically squeeze into a size six, it is equally as futile (and uncomfortable) to have the same expectation with body size."

- Evelyn Tribole & Elyse Resch,
authors of Intuitive Eating

Isn't it strange that most of the time most of us don't have a problem accepting our heights, our eye colour or the size of our hands? This doesn't mean that you're completely happy with these features, nor does it mean that you've never wanted to change them, but most of the time we just accept them because we know that there's nothing that we can do about them. So why is it that we have an issue accepting our bodies?

The reality is that everyone is born with a natural body shape. Some people have short slim legs, some have long muscular legs, some have an hour glass shape and others don't. One of the first topics that I talk about when I teach my workshops is to accept and respect your body's natural shape, because if you don't there's always going to be a part of you that will remain unfulfilled, and think that you can't be happy because you're not a particular shape. Right from childhood, I had always wanted a body like the actresses on television, but it didn't matter how much I tried, I just couldn't get myself to look like them. The reason for this was very simple: I had natural curves in certain places, and unless I planned to surgically remove half my body and reconstruct the other half, I would have this natural shape for life.

A person's natural body shape will begin to emerge when they start to listen to and respond to their bodies carefully. People who naturally maintain a healthy weight are very in tune with their natural body signals. These people don't diet, but they are simply so in touch with themselves when it comes to hunger and eating, they rarely ever get to a point of starving, and rarely ever overeat. These people do not eat for reasons other than hunger (most of the time), hence they are not engaged in any form of emotional or unconscious eating.

PUTTING IT INTO PRACTICE

1. Remember that everyone has their own unique shape and body type.
    Learn to stop battling with your natural shape, and work on accepting it -
    you will find that this will bring you much inner peace.

2. If you're having trouble identifying what you may look like at your natu-
    ral blueprint shape, have a close look at your body. What sort of shape
    do you have? Do have a smaller waist than hips? Are your legs strong and
    muscular, or are they thinner in shape? What height are you? Is there
    anybody in your family who is naturally slim that seems to have the same
    body shape as you? This will be a clue for you. If you can't find anyone in
    your family, have a look around you at some real life women, who seems
    to resemble your shape? This may be a good indication of your natural
    body shape.

I AM CONNECTED TO MY HUNGER

I like the fact that I can feel my hunger and I am grateful for this amazing mechanism

I recognise and acknowledge that there is a difference between physical and emotional hunger

I no longer fear any hunger because hunger is a signal that tells me that I want to live, it's a signal that connects me to life again.

I am now able to nourish myself in the appropriate manner as I am able to connect with and feel my hunger clearly

I acknowledge that my emotional hunger can never be satisfied with food, but rather I yearn to be satisfied through the joy of life

I am blessed to be connected

I AM CONNECTED TO MY HUNGER

4

FEEL THE PHYSICAL HUNGER AND EAT

"Hunger is simply a signal from your body's intelligence that it wishes to eat and is prepared for the proper metabolism of the food that is to be consumed"

- Deepak Chopra

When you feel physical hunger, eat.

Can you imagine trying to keep your eyes open when your body is crying out for sleep? Or would you ever deny yourself the opportunity to use the toilet when you really needed to go? My guess is that you've probably answered 'no' to both the questions. (If you ever did try to go against your body's natural requirements, eventually your body would get its own way anyway. *I mean, how long can you go without a pee?*)

So why is it that most of us would never deny ourselves the need to sleep, or excrete, but yet deny ourselves the need to satisfy our physical hunger? We probably wouldn't tolerate being told when we should use the toilet or sleep, but why when it comes to eating, do we allow others to dictate how much we eat? The fact of the matter is that we rely on our bodies to keep us alive. We trust that our heart will continue to beat and that we will remember to breathe, but we don't trust our bodies enough to be able to guide us to eat properly.

To establish a healthy relationship with food, we have to come to terms with the fact that physical hunger is a natural signal for us to eat. It is a message from our body telling us that it is ready to metabolise food. (Similarly, when you eat when you are not hungry, your body simply is not ready to metabolise the food.) It's a little similar to filling up your car with fuel. It makes sense to fill up when your car is low on fuel. Filling it up when it's already full doesn't make any sense and aside from an overflow, it doesn't really achieve anything worthwhile. It is very possible that if you've been on a number of diets, you may have temporarily lost the ability to pick up on this signal, but once you start to listen to what your body is saying, you'll soon be able to tune in to it again. It does require mindfulness and it may take practice, but it is possible.

If you have engaged in dieting for a long time, the concept of eating when you are hungry may seem very alien to you. Chances are you are so used to being told when to eat, and when not to eat, that you may have forgotten what natural hunger feels like. To help you do this, I would like to introduce a hunger scale to you. It will help you to become more aware of what level of hunger you are feeling.

S - Stuffed

6 - Overeaten

5 - Full

4 - Satisfied

3 - Neutral

2 - Peckish

1 - Hungry

E - Empty

Level E: EMPTY - This is when you're at your hungriest, you're empty. You could eat anything. At this point, you may well experience some physical symptoms such as, feeling faint, dizzy or perhaps a little nauseated. Your concentration may also be effected.

Level 1: HUNGRY - This is when you are nice and hungry, and you know pretty soon, you're going to be at empty. For many people this would be a good time to eat as your body is ready to digest the food, and as a result, the food tastes delicious. (You may have noticed that food always tends to taste better when you are actually hungry). Also because you are hungry, it will be easier for you to note the signal of fullness as there is a clear difference between the two.

Level 2: PECKISH - You're mildly hungry. For some people, they prefer to eat at this level, having a few bites and then stopping until they are mildly hungry again. For many people this level is an indication that they will be properly hungry and ready to eat soon.

Level 3: NEUTRAL - You are neither hungry nor full.

Level 4: SATISFIED – You start to feel your hunger subsiding. For some people, this is a feeling they experience after a meal.

Level 5: FULL - People experience being full differently. Some people will stop eating at the *satisfied* level whereas others would prefer the few extra bites until they are comfortably full. Remember to experiment with your hunger and fullness levels, find what works best for you. The likelihood is that you will be most comfortable when you stop eating at levels 4 or 5.

LEVEL 6: OVEREATEN – You've gone a few bites past full, and you are beginning to feel uncomfortable after the meal.

Level S: STUFFED – There are different levels in this category, ranging from overeating to nauseated. As with level E, I'd recommend that you try not to get to this level often.

Most of the naturally slim people that I have interviewed have said that they don't like to get to level E because they will eat anything at this point. It's like they go into a *survival* mode, eating whatever comes their way. Most of them said that they tend to overeat, sometimes even to level S in this circumstance because their pace of eating tends to increase, and hence they often eat past the 'satisfied 'or 'full' level.

This behaviour may also be present amongst dieters or overeaters, especially after a binge. For example many people often feel guilty after overeating, and then attempt to restrict their food intake to balance it out. However, not being able to stay hungry for too long, they often plunge straight back into overeating again, and the cycle continues.

THERE IS A DIFFERENCE BETWEEN EMOTIONAL HUNGER AND BODY HUNGER

Recognising your emotional hunger will bring to your attention a huge illusion: that acquiring more of something will never bring you prolonged happiness. For some people, when they first come to the realisation that they can eat whenever they are hungry, they experience panic. They worry that with this sort of freedom, they'll eat all the time. This isn't the case.

Nobody eats *all* the time.

Don't you think it's really interesting how we can trust our bodies to:

- Pump the blood around our body in the correct way

- Ensure that we remember to breathe

- Heal a cut when we start to bleed

- Regenerate itself by producing new cells

- Regulate a correct temperature for our body

- Have its own built in central processing unit (the brain)

We trust ourselves to take care of essential functions right from our body temperature to our blood pressure, but when it comes down to it, we have difficulty in trusting our bodies when it comes to eating. We get scared that if we give our body permission to eat when it gets physically hungry, it'll somehow just continue to eat, and eat (what we perceive to be) the wrong stuff.

When we become hungry, it is important for us to identify where that hunger originates. I believe that we experience two types of hunger: the first is what I call 'Body Hunger', which is physiological in nature. This is when we are prompted to eat for the purpose of nourishing ourselves, and it is the only real reason that we should be eating. The second type of hunger is what I refer to as 'Emotional Hunger'. This kind of hunger is not prompted by a physiological need for the food, but rather to satisfy us in another way. It's often this kind of hunger that keeps us eating for the wrong reasons and keeps the weight on. Let's explore the difference between the two:

Body Hunger

From a purely physical perspective, food is simply nourishment for the body. No more, no less. I read a wonderful message some time ago that said, "food was not intended to be fun, it was intended to nourish the body."

Physical hunger is gradual and usually shows itself with physical symptoms, for example a grumbling stomach. If you are extremely hungry, you may also experience headaches or irritability.

If you listen carefully enough, it will tell you the type of food that it is hungry for and when it has had enough.

To hear the signal from the body, you need to tune into your body carefully and start to recognise the signals.

Emotional Hunger

Mind hunger may come on as an urgent call for food, as opposed to the body hunger's gradual onset.

May prompt you eat when you are encountering emotional discomfort, including boredom.

May prompt you to eat when you're not hungry and you see a food that you love. In this case, your mouth wants to experience the taste of the food, not your body.

It is the nature of your mind to be under the false illusion of always 'wanting'. It will make you feel the following: "If I just had that car, that relationship, that partner, that bagel, cake etc., then I would feel better and everything will be okay". Understand that mind hunger will fool you into eating. But keep in mind that the chase is more alluring than the acquisition.

Learn to identify its voice, and you'll be well on your way to your natural blueprint weight. (This will be covered in more detail later.)

BEWARE OF CLOCK-WATCHING

We are creatures of habit and to break free we have to make a conscious effort of being aware at all times. When my client Jenny was new to the concepts of *My Secret Affair with Chocolate Cake*, she used to watch the clock and hope that she would get hungry soon. Occasionally, when her favourite food was available and it was an 'acceptable' time to eat, she would actually manage to persuade herself to eat it, even though she wasn't yet feeling hungry. She says that she literally used to 'fool herself' into being hungry. Although it took her some time to realise what she was doing, she noticed that subconsciously she was still eating according to the clock.

Whilst it can seem easier to eat according to the clock, you are still allowing an external source to dictate when you are eating. In order to truly reconnect with your body, you need to acknowledge and respect the message that it is giving you. Many of my clients find that they eat a lot less when they start listening to their body and quite often their body adjusts into a new routine. Remember, just because we are taught that we must eat at certain times, doesn't necessarily mean that we will be hungry at those times.

PUTTING IT INTO PRACTICE

1. The thing to remember is that everyone's eating pattern will be different, and only you can determine what works for you. I would recommend that you explore the different levels and find what works for you. Start to notice how the food tastes when you eat at the different levels of the hunger scale. How does the food taste when you are really hungry compared with when you are full? How does the food feel in your stomach at these different times? Use the *Reconnection Guide* at the end of this chapter to help you.

2. If the reconnection process is new to you, then it may be an idea to stop and reconnect with your body every couple of hours to see where you are on the hunger scale and how you are feeling. You can do this by closing your eyes, taking a few deep breaths, and bringing your attention to your stomach. How does it feel? Are you ready to eat? If so, what does the hunger feel like to you? Remember that hunger is gradual and it's not a feeling that comes on all of a sudden. If you've eaten a satisfying meal only an hour ago, then you need to really tune in and ask yourself whether it's food you're hungry for, or something else.

3. Following on from the point above, you need to realise that if you are eating to the point of satisfaction on the hunger scale, then you may well become hungry again in a few hours, and if this is the case, then welcome the hunger and the call to eat. Don't be afraid of the hunger, because if you are eating just enough for the feeling of hunger to subside, then you may feel the need to eat again soon. This also works in reverse. If you have eaten to the point of fullness or above, then it may well take longer for the hunger to show up again. Many of my clients experience this. Quite often they stop eating when they reach the point of fullness, then as they learn how to nourish their emotional hunger, they slowly learn how to stop at the point of satisfaction. I continually find that people are always amazed when they start to tune into their hunger and satiety signals properly, because they suddenly realise that there is a big difference between how much they used to eat, and how much they

actually require. So, if you are new to this approach, or have been in the habit of overeating, then you may have to apply some logic to the situation. If you have eaten a sufficient amount of food and feel hungry again after an hour, you need to ask yourself whether you are experiencing real body hunger.

4. Remember that eating when you are hungry means exactly that: eating when you are hungry. In order to honour your body's hunger, it may be helpful to plan ahead. Many of my clients have benefited from the following piece of advice: buy yourself a little food bag or container, fill it up with foods that you enjoy eating and keep it with you at all times. Make sure you always have food available as this will ensure that you don't reach level E on the hunger scale too often.

5. Sometimes you may have to apply some logic to the situation at hand. If you know you get hungry at a certain time in the morning and it's impossible for you to eat at that time, then it may be a better idea to have a smaller snack beforehand whenever you can, as this will stop you from reaching level E on the hunger scale. For example, when I was used to teach in Primary Schools, I never used to eat in the mornings because I was never hungry enough before the kids came in. However, by the mid-morning break I was ready to eat anything and everything! If I am faced with a similar situation now, I usually eat a small snack - even if I am not completely hungry, as this stops me from overeating later in the day. If you find yourself in a similar situation, use your judgement about making an appropriate decision. Don't leave yourself open to any overeating triggers.

6. The very next time you become hungry, take some time out and stop for a moment. Connect with your body and ask yourself where you are feeling the hunger, are you really feeling body hunger, or could it be the mind hunger creeping in?

7. Keep well hydrated. Sometimes people mistake thirst for body hunger. Ensure you drink enough water during the day. (If you are not sure how much you should be drinking, consult an appropriate professional who will be able to help you.)

THE RECONNECTION GUIDE

Use the following guide to help you reconnect with your body's natural hunger signals. Points 1 &2 should be considered before eating and points 3& 4 should be considered after you have eaten.

1. How hungry are you feeling? (If you need to, close your eyes, and bring your attention to your stomach and just feel.)

    ....
    ....
    ....
    ....

2. How does the hunger feel in your body?

    ....
    ....
    ....
    ....

3. How did the food taste when you first started to eat, and what happened to the taste as you continued eating?

    ....
    ....
    ....
    ....

4. How does your body feel now that you have eaten?

    ....
    ....
    ....
    ....

I EXPERIENCE PLEASURE WHEN I EAT

Food is a pleasure to be enjoyed.

I like the fact that I can taste flavours and make choices based on how the food feels in my body.

I look forward to eating all my meals with enjoyment.

There are so many tastes and so many varieties to sample, and I look forward to discovering more about the different foods.

Enjoying my food is a way for me to enjoy the present moment, it is a way for me to connect with life.

I enjoy looking at my food and taking in the aroma before my mouth samples the taste.

I EXPERIENCE PLEASURE WHEN I EAT

5

SHOWING UP FOR YOUR MEALTIMES...
TASTING EACH MOUTHFUL

"I find it hard to overeat when I fully engage in the experience of eating. Put time aside for your food, and appreciate this joyous experience with all your heart."

- Nisha Pattani

It's amazing to think that throughout all our dieting and bingeing, many of us hardly ever take the time out to actually taste our food. Eating should be a pleasurable experience, and it can only be that when we actually decide to show up for our own mealtimes, which means acknowledging that we are *actually* eating. If we fail to taste and appreciate our food properly, then although we may experience physiological fullness, we may still be left feeling a psychological dissatisfaction, and hence crave more food. A vital part of establishing a healthy relationship with food comes from being present whilst eating.

Tasting each mouthful means...

1. **Noticing That You are Eating**

    The first step is to acknowledge that you are eating. For example, one of the biggest changes that came about whilst I was healing my relationship with food was that I starting noticing how much unconscious eating I was actually doing. I may have nibbled something out of the fridge, or tasted the food whilst cooking it, or eaten a chocolate whilst rushing to work. Although there isn't anything wrong with doing any of these things, the issue was that I didn't really count it as eating. I would then continue to eat all my meals as usual, not really listening to my body. It was as if I was on an auto-pilot response.

    As you start to become more aware of your eating, you'll have the choice to decide whether you really want to eat at this moment, or not. You'll start to question whether you're really hungry or not, you'll even start to wonder if you actually like the food or not. (You may find that eating yesterday's cold leftovers straight from the fridge, and then washing them down with flat lemonade because they got stuck in your throat may not be so appealing anymore.) Next time you decide to eat, stop for a moment and decide what you want to eat. Once you have decided, prepare the food, sit down and put your attention into eating. Spend a little while looking at the food and taking in its aroma. When you put the food into your mouth, notice how it feels and tastes. Make sure you spend enough time chewing the food, as not only does this make the eating experience more focused, but it also aids digestion. Try not to ingest another mouthful until you have swallowed the current one and note how this process makes you feel. For some people it will be pleasurable, and for others it may feel strange and they may become impatient.

It is also worth noting that slowing down the eating process will give your brain time to register how much food you have eaten, and whether you are full or not. Although I feel it would be very beneficial if you could be fully aware all the time whilst eating, I appreciate that this may be difficult for some people to do. Therefore, do what feels right to you. As long as you are following your body signals, and tasting the food, it's a step in the right direction.

2.   **Pay Attention to the Taste of Each Mouthful.**

For some people, tasting each mouthful will help them to determine how full they are. Notice that when you are hungry and begin to eat, each mouthful tastes delicious. However, towards the end of your meal the food usually doesn't taste as good, and this is one way of your body telling you that you have eaten enough. You may find that you can sense this more easily with some foods compared with others.

I realised how powerful this point was a few years ago when I was holidaying in Rhodes. One evening when I was feeling extremely hungry, I remember looking at the menu and thinking to myself that I wasn't really keen on any of the choices available. After some deliberation I decided to go for the chicken dish. To my surprise, when the food arrived it tasted delicious, but I also remember that around half way into the meal, it stopped tasting so good, so I decided to stop eating it. My body was giving me a signal loud and clear that it was satisfied. Ever since that incident, I have become more aware of how tasting each mouthful consciously tells me how satisfied my body really is, sometimes before I even recognise the feeling in my stomach. It came to my attention whilst conducting research for this book that naturally slim people eat this way much of the time. As part of the research, I interviewed quite a few of my naturally slim friends. I remember one of them commenting that she gets 'bored' with a particular taste after a while and loses interest in the food and she knows that this is her cue to stop.

Now, although this was quite a reliable indicator of fullness for me, I later discovered something quite interesting. I found that certain foods continued to taste divine in my mouth, even though my stomach was clearly full, and sometimes even stuffed. Sometimes I would be almost sick from eating, but my mouth wanted more of the particular food that I was eating. After doing some research, I found that some foods may have addictive qualities for some people. If you are finding it difficult to stop eating a particular food, even once you are full, then you need to think about the effect that that particular food is having on your body. Susie Orbach, author of *On Eating* writes:

> *"Perhaps you are responding to the sugar and salt in the food and the chemical receptors in your brain crave more of those flavourings. Your salt and sugar receptors are working overtime and will never be satisfied. Once you have gone beyond a small portion, there actually is no right amount. It becomes hard for you to stop because you are not responding to your hunger, but to a craving that has been induced by the salt or sugar."*

There have also been a number of studies performed on rats which suggest that excessive sugar intake may function in similar ways to other addictive substances[8]. I don't think this necessarily means that you have to avoid these foods altogether, but I do think you need to be very aware of how these foods make your body feel. Once you are aware, you can then decide how you want to tackle the challenge. One of the strategies that you could use is to eat the food before you eat your normal meal. For example, if chocolate brings on an addictive tendency, you could try eating it before you eat your main meal, (this is like eating your dessert before your main meal). Quite often, once you have eaten your main meal, you'll find that you'll no longer crave the chocolate.

---

8 Boscarsly, M. (2009) Sugar Addiction, More than Just a Sweet Tooth? Summer 2009, Vol.4, issue 2 www.foodethicscouncil.org

3.   Tasting Each Mouthful Helps to Keep you Present

Tasting each mouthful will also help to keep you present in what you are doing. I don't really think it matters how you look at overeating or dieting, ultimately people become stuck in a cycle of dieting or overeating because they are identifying with their minds. The fact of the matter is that when that moment comes where you are about to overeat, right then you a have a choice. Are you going to take the step and eat, or are you going to refrain from the extra spoonful? That moment is the only moment in which you can make that decision. Quite often, many people tell themselves that they'll overeat just for today, and then start the diet again tomorrow. They are not in the present moment, but instead making themselves feel better by envisioning a 'better, thinner' tomorrow. If you choose to keep repeating this action, you'll constantly find yourself overeating.

Therefore, tasting each mouthful will help to bring you back to the present moment. Once you start to realise that the present moment is the only moment that you will ever have, you'll realise it's what you do right now that counts. It's the choices that you make on a moment-to-moment basis that shape your tomorrow. On a philosophical note, it's also worth considering that *tomorrow* will never really come, because all you ever have is the *now*. Therefore in order to bring about a more desirable *now*, it's what you do in the present moment that counts. Start eating as if you're already at your natural body shape, because that's what will bring the desired result about.

4.   Slow Down

In order to taste each mouthful, you will have slow to down your eating. When you eat slower you'll find that you require less food, and become satisfied quicker. Remember that eating should be pleasurable and you should *really* enjoy the whole experience. Appreciate the way that the food looks, tastes, smells and feels. The key is to enjoy every bite and be aware of how your body feels.

5.   Become aware of external cues.

Have you ever considered what makes you eat? Although we give consideration to internal cues (such as emotions and physiological hunger), many of us don't realise that external cues also play a part. For example, have you ever found yourself overeating when you have family or friends around? Or do you frequently find yourself eating until your plate is empty? There are many external cues like the ones I have just mentioned that prompt people to eat when they are not hungry. In order to lose weight effectively, you will need to become mindful of these external cues and take action to ensure that you do not succumb to their calling.

A study carried out by Wansink (2009)[9] and his graduate students highlighted that people ate more popcorn if they were given a larger bucket compared with a medium sized bucket – even when the popcorn was five days old and stale! This particular study offered everyone who bought a ticket for a matinee movie, a free soft drink along with either a large or a medium sized bucket of popcorn, which was five days old. (Both the buckets were deliberately set to be large enough so that nobody would be able to finish all the popcorn.) In exchange for the free popcorn and soft drink, the participants were asked to answer a few questions after the movie. Upon learning the truth behind the study, most participants felt that they had not eaten according to external cues, feeling that they could not be so easily fooled. However, when the buckets full of the remaining popcorn were weighed, it was found that the participants eating from the bigger buckets consumed an average of 53% more popcorn. The study concluded that the staleness of the popcorn meant that the participants were not eating for the taste, and due to the fact that many of them had eaten lunch shortly before the movie had started, they were not eating due to hunger either, but instead consumed more popcorn if they were given the bigger buckets.

Another popular external cue (or shall we say, *eat me now* cue), is how much people eat when they can actually see the food. There was another interesting study carried out[10], in which a number of office secretaries were given their own personal stash of Hershey's Kisses (chocolates). The treats were displayed in two types of bowls: a transparent type and a white opaque type, where the chocolates could not be easily seen. It was found that the secretaries who were given the transparent bowls consumed an extra 77 calories per day[11].

---

9 Wansink, B. (2009) Mindless Eating – Why We Eat More Than We Think. Hay House Publishers, UK.

10 Wansink, B. (2009) Mindless Eating – Why We Eat More Than We Think. Hay House Publishers, UK

11 Please note that I have talked about calories only to make a point, not because you should be focussing on them.

I have shared these studies with you in order for you to start thinking about what external cues may be causing you to eat. One of the external cues that I really struggled with at the start was practicing mindful eating when eating out at restaurants. Once I realised how much food my body physically required, I found it difficult dealing with the portion sizes. I found myself rushing my food so that I could finish all of it before my brain had the chance to register that I was full. It took me a long while to work out that I was having difficulty dealing with the fact that there was so much food on my plate, and I just couldn't slow myself down enough to savour the food and then stop when I was satisfied. So, I started to cut my portions in half and put the rest out of sight. It worked. When I had the smaller amount of food to focus on, I was able to savour my food without having to worry about finishing the rest.

PUTTING IT INTO PRACTICE

1. Try putting down the cutlery in between bites, (or put your food down if you're using your hands). Quite often when we eat, we don't get to savour each bite because we are too busy preparing the next bite. By putting your cutlery or food down for a few moments, it gives you the chance to register and taste the food already in your mouth. Ask yourself how many flavours you can taste and whether each bite still tastes as delicious as the first bite that you took. It's worth remembering that for many people, the taste of the food is an indicator of fullness.

2. Following on from the first point, the next tip is to stop in the middle of your meal, put your fork down and wait a few seconds. Restaurant servings tend to be a lot bigger than our bodies actually require. When you start eating again, notice how the food tastes in your mouth. Is it still as delicious as it was before? If not, this may be your cue to stop.

3. How long can you make each bite last? As an experiment, see how long you can make each bit last and notice how the taste of the food changes. Some of my clients love doing this with chocolate as they find they only need a little bit to satisfy them. I have also found (both personally and through clients), that many convenience foods lose their taste after being in the mouth for a while. Once the initial strong flavouring has worn off, what remains is something quite tasteless, and this is what often propels people to experiment with different foods.

4. Have fun the Spanish way – Tapas. Personally, I love variety, so this option is great for someone like me! Put a small selection of all your favourite foods onto a platter and have fun savouring each bite. You can make the choices as wacky and wonderful as you like, adding some olives, chocolate, bread, or luscious cherry tomatoes if you like. If you fancy some company, have an evening where you invite some friends and they can all bring their favourite dish and share. Just remember to remain mindful whilst eating!

5. Take as much of the food as you think you need and put the rest of it out of sight, as having more food on the plate may act as an external cue to eat. You may find that you only have to do this for a short while as you adjust to this new way of eating. Once you realign with your natural hunger and satiety signals again and lose the preoccupation with food, you'll no longer need to practice this tip.

I AM FREE

I enjoy knowing that I am in charge of making my own food choices

I acknowledge that we are all built uniquely and I know I am the only one who knows what's best for me

I love having the freedom to explore all the aisles of the supermarket

I love having the freedom to appreciate my body

I am free to enjoy the pleasure of eating

I AM FREE

6

GIVE YOURSELF PERMISSION TO EAT WHATEVER YOU WANT

"Chocolate cake eaten because you are hungry for it in your mouth and in your stomach can be relished"

- Susie Orbach

Yes, you read the title correctly. *Give yourself permission to eat whatever you want.*

How do you feel about eating whatever you want? Many of my clients are terrified when they discover that this process involves making their own choices about food. What I find amazing is that a vast majority of these people have significant responsibilities in their lives, such as bringing up children, or the responsibility of their career. But somehow, the idea of eating whatever they want really frightens them. It is as if they cannot trust themselves around food, and that if they did allow themselves complete permission to eat whatever they wanted, they fear that they may end up eating forever.

But why does this happen? Well, the main issue is that on some level you don't trust yourself to be able to feed yourself appropriately, and the dieting industry further re-enforces this belief by conveying to you what you can and cannot eat. Diets make you believe you cannot be trusted to establish and maintain your natural blueprint weight. They set you up to fail because they promote black-and-white thinking, and make you believe that you have to rely on them in order to be at a desirable weight.

The truth however is that you have the power and the wisdom within you to make the desired changes, and the only way that you will make these changes is to have more self-love and self-belief in yourself. You can be trusted to feed yourself appropriately - if you just give yourself a chance.

What to expect when you start to eat whatever you want

To begin with, most people go through a phase where they choose to eat all their favourite foods. This happens because for the first time after years of dieting, they are allowing themselves full permission to eat. It's almost as if they have to get this phase out 'of their system' before they can move on. This some-times can be a difficult thing to do because some people may fear that they will put more weight on. However, if you are truly listening to and honouring your body, eventually at some point you will start to make healthier choices because you'll start to respect how you feel after eating a particular food. (Remember that one of the foundations discussed in chapter one was the fact that our natu-ral state is one of well-being. If we give ourselves a chance, we will be steered towards our natural state.)

A Caution...

EATING WHATEVER YOU WANT DOES NOT MEAN EATING WHATEVER YOU WANT, IN WHICHEVER QUANTITY YOU WANT, WITHOUT TAKING INTO CONSIDERATION HOW YOUR BODY FEELS!

I can't stress this enough. When I first came across the concept of eat-ing whatever I wanted, I thought I was in paradise. I became lost in the 'airy-fairyness' of the whole thing, and it didn't work for me the way that I thought it would. Why? Because I didn't commit fully to becoming an expert on myself. I only followed half the advice. I ate whatever I wanted without taking into con-sideration how my body felt. I didn't pay any attention to my energy levels, nor did I give a second thought to the fact that I was compelled to eat sugar every day. That was the biggest mistake that I made, and that is why I failed to begin with. So, I am sharing this with you because I do not want you to make the same mistake that I did.

The idea of giving yourself permission to eat whatever you want should be an opening for you to discover which foods work well with your body, and which foods don't. If you begin to work in harmony with your body instead of against it, you will yield results.

Remember: Addressing the body alone is not the whole story...

It's also worth remembering that although I have started off by sharing with you the basics about how we may want to be eating, it's not the whole story. There may well be some of you that might find it difficult to grasp this concept, but keep in mind the way you think and feel has a lot to do with the bigger picture...hang in there – it's covered a little further on in the book!

PUTTING IT INTO PRACTICE

1. Give yourself permission to eat what you want

Give yourself permission to eat whatever you want. Bingeing can often arise because you have deprived yourself of certain foods 'legally' for so long. For example, if I say to you: "Whatever you do, don't think of a pink elephant," what have you just done? Thought of a pink elephant. Similarly, if you're told you can't eat a particular food, you'll find that you're more attracted to it, and when you do allow yourself to eat it, you're more likely to binge on it as you may feel that you've fallen off the 'being good with food' wagon. If you really want to stop overeating and restore balance, you need to give yourself choices, and you can only make a choice when you have permission to eat whatever you want.

Many people find this very difficult to do when they first decide to abandon dieting, and this is because they think they have given themselves permission to eat whatever they want, but in reality they are still operating from the diet mentality. Tina, one of my clients once told me that when she first started this journey, she would allow herself to eat an ice-lolly as long as it only had 99 calories in it, but eating her favourite ice-cream was going too far. The key is to really listen to and respond accordingly to your body, and focus on pushing that 'diet voice' out of the equation. The bottom line is simply this: if you are still depriving yourself of what your body truly wants, then the avenue for overeating will still be present.

Whilst re-discovering my natural blueprint weight, I found out something very bizarre. When I used to count calories (quite often I would give myself a maximum of 1500 a day), I found I was thinking about food all the time, obsessively counting the calories. Eating out was a real problem, and most of the time, I wished that I had a higher allowance. Anyway, I could only manage this type of 'deprivation' for a few days or perhaps a week at a stretch, after which time I would binge excessively. Now here's the ironic thing: when I started to allow myself to eat whatever my body desired, I actually consumed between 1200 - 1500 calories most of the time. What I had previously thought of as 'deprivation', was now balanced and more than satisfactory. It's funny really - things tend to work out when you let go of the outcome.

2.   *'Overloading'* vs. the *'Thinking time* 'option.

One of the most common questions that clients will ask me is: "*How* do I give myself permission to eat whatever I want?" Good question - one that I wish that I'd had the answer to when I first started this journey.

I did a lot of reading and research on how to realign with my natural blueprint shape again, and one of the suggestions that I was given was to buy a lot of my favourite food and keep it in the house. (I call this the 'overloading' method. In fact, it was suggested that I buy so much of the food that I couldn't physically consume it all even if I wanted to. I assume that the reasoning behind this suggestion is to eliminate the feeling of deprivation: If you don't feel deprived of the food, then you won't be drawn to eating it all the time either.)

So, I gave it go. It didn't work. I tried again. It didn't work. In fact, I broke a new record - I did manage to consume all the food. The more I tried to implement it, the worse it became for me. To further complicate the issue, I kept on finding success stories where people had managed to implement this step and drop the weight!

Anyway, it took me a while to realise that maybe this 'overloading' method wasn't going to work for me. For some reason, I wasn't yet in a place where I could trust myself with having lots of my favourite food around me. It was doing me more damage. So instead, I decided to change my strategy. I told myself that if my body was really hungry for a particular food, then I would let myself eat it – even if it meant going out to purchase it. The fact that I had to make an effort to go out and buy the food made me think twice about whether I really wanted to eat it or not. This method worked for me because it gave me a bit of time to both tune into my body signals, as well as reflect on my thoughts, (hence the name, 'Thinking Time' option).

Now, before we move on, there is something interesting that I want you to note here. Do you remember earlier in the book I mentioned that there were different degrees of emotional eating? Well, looking back at my history I would say that I experienced chronic emotional eating, and the reason that the 'overloading' method didn't work for me was because once I started to eat sugar, I wanted more of it. It didn't matter how much I tried to make peace with lots of chocolate in the house, I still ended up eating it.

It took me a long while to figure out that my issue was not just of a 'psychological nature'. In other words, it wasn't just about the deprivation, I actually feel that my body adjusted to wanting more sugar. So, I had to make a conscious choice to honour my body and to think carefully about consuming sugary foods. I didn't completely stop eating the sugary foods, I just became more aware of how my body felt and then made decisions based on that.

Now, because I don't think that there's a *wrong* or *right* way to implement this whole approach, it's up to you to find out what works for you. I have had clients who have been very comfortable with the idea of 'overloading'[12] on a particular food, and for these individuals the main issue has been one of mostly deprivation. These individuals have found that with this approach the food loses its power over them because they can eat it whenever they want.

If, on the other hand, you find that it's difficult for you to stop eating a particular food, even past the physical satisfaction point, then it may be an idea to choose the 'Thinking Time' option. This way, you still give yourself the freedom to eat whatever you want, but allow yourself some reflection time.

3.   **Allow yourself to explore *ALL THE AISLES* of the supermarket**

There was a time when I hardly visited the crisps, chocolate or fresh cream cake sections on a normal shopping trip because I was not "legally" allowed to eat these foods. (Unless of course, I was entertaining, or it was for a binge, in which case the rest of the Supermarket was non-existent.) Part of restoring balance to your eating pattern is about giving yourself permission to shop for whatever it is that you want. So next time you go shopping, take some time out to browse around the

---

12 Please note however, that by 'overloading' I do not mean that you physically eat all the food. What I mean is that you buy a lot of the food and eat it within the boundaries of hunger and physical satisfaction. (This is not an invitation to eat as much of it as you can in hope that you'll get sick of it and never want to touch it again).

whole of the food store. Get used to the idea that nothing is off-limits for you anymore. Take some time to explore all the sections. How does this make you feel?

4.   **Take responsibility for the way your body feels**

If you're intending to reach your blueprint weight, you will have to take full responsibility for the way that your body feels. People who have attained their natural blueprint weight are very in touch with the way that their bodies feel and react to certain foods. These people will not eat something if it is not in harmony with their bodies. Most of the time, they eat whatever they want as long as they feel well. Also be aware of the fact that it's not necessarily just the so-called 'junk foods' that always produce disharmony. My Dad, for example, reacts to garlic and my grandmother has trouble with salad sometimes. Everyone's body is different, and it's up to you to determine how a particular food feels in your body.

5.   **Keep a food diary to figure out how certain foods make you feel.**

A good way to start to reconnect with your body again is to keep a food diary. The intention here is not to track how much you're eating or whether you're within your "limit," but rather to help you become an expert on you. The action of writing things down will help you to become more conscious of the choices that you're making. You may want to observe the following:

- The Time – This is useful because you can see how long it takes before you start to experience real physical hunger again after your last meal. If you find that you're wanting to eat on an hourly basis, then you have to question whether you're experiencing true physical hunger or whether it's just emotional hunger.

- What You Have Eaten and How You Feel about It – This will help you to break the dieting mentality and choose foods that your body truly wants. How you're feeling about what you're eating is also very important and will be discussed further on in the book.

- How Your Body Feels – Be honest with yourself here. How does the food feel in your body? To begin with, it may be an idea to check in with your body an hour after you've eaten to see where your energy levels are at. If you feel sluggish or sleepy, then perhaps other food choices may be better options.

Over the next few weeks allow yourself to eat all your favourite foods, and make a note of how these foods feel in your body. I would recommend buying a pocket notebook to record your observations. I am not suggesting that you turn this into some sort of a diet, but I am saying that you start to become an expert on you. Become your own detective. Experiment with eating different types of foods. How does your body react to carbohydrates, proteins, or sugar? What effect do these different foods have on your ability to concentrate? How well and alive do you feel? Please remember that what your mouth enjoys is not necessarily what your body enjoys!

6. **Be patient with yourself whilst you are discovering your new relationship with food**

I think it's important to remember to remain patient whilst you are finding out for yourself, what works and what doesn't. Chances are if you're only just discovering a healthy relationship with food, you will make some mistakes. As I pointed out previously, everyone's body is different, and people require different things. During the early stages of your reconnection process, you may think you want a particular food, have it, and then discover it wasn't quite the right one. Don't worry over this too much; you will get better at responding to your body signals.

I know one lady who has successfully dropped seven dress sizes using this approach, and she told me that she found it very odd when she started to crave blackberries as she's never eaten them before! We could only conclude that our bodies are amazing tools.

7. **Quick visualisation before you decide what to eat**

I've found it's a good idea to actually take time out before you prepare a meal and ask yourself what it is that you want to eat. Ideally when you eat, you want to try and fulfil two requirements: the first is obviously satisfying your physical hunger; and the second is satisfying your psychological hunger. Satisfying your physical hunger is fairly straight forward, because it doesn't matter what food you put into your body, at some point you will become full, (be it lettuce or burgers). However, satisfying your psychological hunger can be somewhat harder to do. Satisfying your psychological hunger will make the ritual of eating complete for you. In order to psychologically satisfy your hunger, you need to ensure that not only are you physically full, but you are completely happy and content with what you have eaten, the food should have completely 'hit the spot'.

For some people if they fail to psychologically satisfy themselves with the food that they consume, they may find themselves overeating to get that feeling of satisfaction.

So how do you ensure that you can psychologically satisfy yourself? Well, take some time out (maybe only 30 or 60 seconds) and think about what type of food your body wants. Do you want something cold, hot or warm? How dense do you want the food to be? Are you in the mood for a prawn salad, or mash potatoes and sausages? How do you want the food to feel in your mouth? Crispy, hard, chewy or smooth? If you think you've got an idea, have a go at visualising your food, how does it make you feel? I remember going to restaurants when I was a compulsive eater. One of the things that really used to wind me up was that no matter what dish I ordered, I always ended up wanting my husband's dish instead. I was baffled at how he always ordered the perfect dish for himself. Then, one day he told me that when he browses through the menu, he actually mentally tastes all the food before making a decision, and that's how he knows what his body wants.

What you may also find is that whilst most of the time you make the correct food choices for yourself, occasionally you may get it wrong. If you find that you've prepared a food, sat down to eat it and no longer want it, then I suggest the following two options: firstly, either put the food away, or freeze it and make something for yourself that you really want. I know this may sound a little crazy but if you were to go ahead and eat it, then the psychological satisfaction would simply not be there and you may soon feel inclined to eat again. The second option I suggest is to just accept that you've made a mistake, decide to forgive yourself, and eat the meal. But, make a conscious decision to resist the urge to eat again if you are not hungry. You may find that you are most likely to exercise this option in a restaurant because it would probably be easier and more economical than ordering another dish.

8.   What if finances are an issue?

This is an important topic which is not covered very often. I have come across people that have financial issues and as a result cannot afford to buy whatever they wish to eat. I think in this situation you can only do the best you can, using the tools that you have. When I experienced this, I had to be very careful that I did not let this issue become a reason for bingeing. Sometimes I used to catch myself thinking that if I couldn't always eat what I wanted then there would no point in eating intuitively, because I wouldn't be following the "rules" properly. Again, without realising, I was turning a non-diet approach into a diet.

After a while (and after much deliberation), I came to the conclusion that I wanted to try and look after and love my body. Therefore, even if I couldn't eat a particular food, I was still willing to eat the alternative, making sure that I would stop when I was full. I kept telling myself that in reality, at that point, I only had two options: carry on bingeing on food that *I didn't even want* because I couldn't start eating 'intuitively' yet; or, accept the fact that although I may not always have the option of eating whatever I wanted, I was willing to at least honour myself when it came to eating when I was hungry and stopping when I was full. It wasn't 100% ideal for me, but it was certainly better than bingeing or dieting.

Just before I conclude this section, I would like to highlight something else that you may want to look out for. Be prepared for the fact that occasionally you may not be in a position to eat whatever it is that you want. (For example, at weddings, parties or perhaps on your way home from work.) If this happens, try to just accept it. After all, you will be hungry again in a few hours and can then eat whatever you want. I have had a few clients who have wanted to experience the perfect meal or snack each time they were hungry, and although there is nothing wrong with this at all, just be careful that you don't upset your equilibrium just because you may have to settle for second best sometimes. Remember it's all about having a healthy relationship with food and keeping a balance.

I AM SATISFIED

I enjoy knowing that I can accurately feel my level of satisfaction.

I feel comfortable when I stop eating as I experience physical satisfaction.

I now lovingly acknowledge that overeating does not lead to satisfaction.

I can easily find ways of satisfying myself that nourish me as a 'whole'.

There is a difference between physical and emotional satisfaction, and I am able to honour both.

I like the fact that life is supposed to be satisfying.

I AM SATISFIED.

7

STOPPING WHEN YOU ARE FULL

"Humanity is under the illusion that more of something is the cause of your happiness. Learn the art of moderation and set yourself free."

- Sunita Pattani

Stopping when full is an important step when it comes to realigning with your natural body shape, but many people seem to struggle with this step. Why?

Because people don't know what 'feeling full' means.

Think back to *The Foundation* in chapter one. The first *Foundation* stated that we needed to consider ourselves as 'whole'. Most individuals will only pay attention to the physical aspect, but 'feeling full' is something that we need to approach from both a physical and an emotional perspective.

Fullness from a physical perspective is when the **body** has had enough to eat. Individuals who are at their natural body weight are very aware of how their body feels when it comes to eating and they respond to these signals accordingly. Most of my clients are astonished at the quantity of food they really require in order to become full, and find themselves reducing the quantity they eat significantly.

The emotional aspect of fullness on the other hand is very different. Most people who want to realign with their natural body shape know that it would serve them better to eat less, but yet somehow they still continue to eat past the point of physical fullness. There's a good reason why...

So far in this book, I have covered with you the physical aspects of eating. In other words: if you change how you eat by listening to your body, your natural blueprint shape will begin to emerge. But, (and it's a big but), *the ultimate key to unlocking your natural body weight and re-establishing a healthy*

relationship with food is not all about the food. It's also about your ability to
connect with your feelings and deal with the underlying trigger that is causing
you to eat. It's also about finding your inner joy.

I kid you not. This is why some people still struggle if they focus solely on
the physical aspects. Yes, you need to be listening and responding to your body
carefully, but if you're not aware of your thoughts and feelings, and if you can't
find your true source of happiness that comes from within, your journey will always be filled with an element of resistance. Believe me, as you begin to become
aware of your thoughts and feelings and as you learn to find the joy in life, your
eating will change and gradually the food won't matter as much to you. You'll
find yourself making healthier choices.

Dr. Dyer expresses this fact beautifully in the opening quote of this chapter
where he states: *"to continue stuffing food into a satiated body is to be trapped
in believing that more of something is the cause of your happiness."* As long as
you keep on using food to numb yourself, and to provide you with the feeling
of instant gratification, you'll never find the true happiness that resides within.
But the day you begin to come to terms with the fact that you're missing a much
deeper connection to yourself, and the fact that you can choose to reconnect
with that part of You again, will be the day that you will begin to unlock your
natural body weight and stay there for good.

What Does Fullness Feel Like? - The Physical Signals

Okay, so back to the physical aspects of fullness. So what does stopping
when you're full actually mean? Well, physiologically speaking, I would say it's
being at level 4 or 5 on the hunger scale. It's when you're no longer hungry,
but you're not too full either, you're just comfortable. (It's also a good idea to
keep in mind that the difference between neutral, satisfied and full is often a
few bites, and the better you get at listening to your body, the more you'll know
when to stop. Usually you will find that the food stops tasting so good.) Listening to your body is the key, and practice strengthens the signal.

When you have eaten enough, your brain will send a signal to your body
to let it know that you are full. You may feel the following signals:

- A gentle satisfied sensation in your solar plexus area (This is the
  area just below your rib cage and above your stomach)

- The feeling of hunger is no longer there

- An inner knowing that you have had enough to eat

- No more food thoughts or signals of hunger

- Your food stops tasting so good and it no longer appeals to you in the way it did when you were hungry

If you have been used to overeating, to begin with, it will probably feel as if you could carry on eating, although you don't need to. However, after a while you'll find you get used to this level of fullness and eating beyond this will feel uncomfortable to you.

Some other points to consider:

Now, you know what the physiological signals of full look like, but what about the other aspects of eating beyond that satisfied point?

One of the first things that I would say is don't fall into the trap of applying 'black and white' thinking when assessing how full you are. As previously mentioned, dieting very much encourages an 'on the wagon-off the wagon' approach, for example, "if you consume this many points, you'll be ok and you won't put the weight on." But what happens if you consume 5 extra points in one day, or three days? You're in the danger zone, better watch it, you might just gain a pound!

The thing you've got to remember about eating until you're satisfied is that there is no external measuring tool to tell you whether you're doing it right or wrong. It's all about how you feel. The main reason I was so unsuccessful at this approach to begin with was because there wasn't an exact number of mouthfuls that I could eat before I knew I was full. There wasn't an automatic alarm bell that suddenly rang in my stomach to say 'full!' – I actually had to think about what I was doing. I had to accept the fact that this was going to be 'hit and miss' at first, and I would have to start off by guessing and listening to when I was full, and it did get easier as time went by.

PUTTING IT INTO PRACTICE

Make sure you're actually hungry before you begin to eat

When your body gets hungry, it's telling you that it's ready to eat and digest the food. If you eat at this point, you'll be able to taste the food a lot better, and eating becomes a very enjoyable, satisfying experience. Your body will then go through a progressive process of becoming full and you'll be able to feel it. This makes it easier for you to stop at the appropriate point for you.

If, on the other hand, you choose to eat when you're not completely hungry, it's unlikely that your body will give you the 'satisfied' signal, until you get to levels 6 or above on the hunger scale.

If you find it difficult to pick up your fullness signals at first, a good tip to use is to ask yourself 'am I still hungry?' Remember to keep in mind Geneen Roth, *"being hungry is a little bit like being in love: if you're not sure, you're probably not!"*

"But the food is tasting so good, I just can't stop – besides, it's not like I eat Chinese takeaway everyday is it?"

Let's get one thing clear: you could eat Chinese takeaway everyday if your body really wanted it (or pizza, or cake, or anything else). What you've got to ask yourself is what is causing that feeling of "I might not get to eat that food again", where is that feeling of deprivation coming from?[13]

You may be surprised at what you find when you take a look at what is causing you to want to overeat that pizza – is it because you think you may not be able to eat it again anytime soon? There is one particular lady that I have interviewed that has struggled with her weight ever since she can remember, (she is in her sixties). When we started to explore what was going on, it became evident that throughout childhood and early adulthood, she experienced quite a

---

13 The reality of the situation is that you get hungry every few hours and you can eat whatever your body wants.

hard working life, and although food was not scarce for her, she didn't have the freedom to eat what she wanted often. So, on the rare occasion when she would indulge in her favourite food, she would eat it until she was stuffed because she wasn't sure when she would get to eat it next. Over the years however, her financial situation has improved ten-fold, but her old habit of scarcity eating is still there. The only issue though, is that she indulges a lot more often than usual, so family gatherings, outings, socialising and weekends are a continuous challenge for her.

If you find yourself in a situation where you're experiencing the 'scarcity eating syndrome,' I would urge you to stop in the middle of your meal, and just listen to what your body is telling you on a physiological level (are you still hungry?). If you find yourself satisfied, then ask yourself what is causing you to want more of the food and reflect on what you're doing. Even if you don't find the answer, it doesn't matter; you still have the choice to stop eating at that point.

If you're eating out with company, put your knife and folk down and focus. You may want to be quiet for a while or engage in conversation – whatever works for you, but it is important that you give yourself space to absorb what's going on inside, both on a physiological and an emotional level. I find that quite often when I am physiologically satisfied and I decide to take a break from eating, for a while, the desire for the food will still remain. But what usually happens is that after a few minutes that desire subsides, and at this point I decide to end my meal by placing my napkin on the plate so that I cannot go back to the food again.

The Clean- Plate Club

There are many people that find it very difficult to stop eating when they have had enough because they are so used to finishing all the food on their plates. This was quite an issue for me (and for many of my clients), because I had been brought-up to finish all the food on my plate, regardless of whether I was full or not.

There are many different reasons why we may be used to finishing the food on our plates. These reasons can range from, *"you can't have dessert until you finish your food"* to *"there are lots of hungry people around the world, so be grateful for what you have."* As a result, we have been programmed to just continue eating, and unfortunately many people are unaware that this could be a significant reason for why they are unable to attain their natural bodily blueprint.

There are a number of strategies which you can use to quit the clean-plate club, and the strategy that you adopt will depend upon your belief system. As usual, my advice would be to do what feels right to you:

- The first thing that you need to realise is that it's ok to leave food on your plate. You only have two choices: one is to leave the food on the plate, and the other is eat the food when your body doesn't require it anymore, which of course may lead to weight gain.

    Many people feel really uncomfortable doing this, so assess the situation you are in. If you are serving dinner at home, it may be an idea to put the food into serving dishes rather than serving it up for everyone. That way, each person is responsible for the amount of food that they put into to their plates. Also, at the beginning, you may be unsure of how much food you need, so you can actually take a little to start with and fill up again if you're still hungry.

- Eating out in a restaurant can be a different story. Think about the portion sizes you get in a restaurant; now consider that your stomach is the size of your fist. Restaurant servings are often larger than you require. So, you can either ask if you can get the food boxed up and brought home, or you may well have to leave some food on the plate – remember you're not responsible for serving that portion up. (Even if it has cost a lot of money, your health and well-being is more important.)

- Another strategy you may want to use in a restaurant is ordering just a starter and perhaps a dessert. Or maybe ordering a starter and sharing a main meal? If the restaurant is happy to do this, then it may be a viable option.

- It's very common for people to participate in the 'clean-plate-club' especially if they are dining out. Many people feel that they are not getting value for money if they do not finish their food. Again you've got to consider the following point: are you willing to put up with the overeating and extra weight to save a few pounds and pennies? Also, think about the fact that dining out is also about the company that you have and the atmosphere of the place. If you are worried about the money aspect, then really think about the restaurant that you are going to and make sure it's worthy of you. Enjoy the surroundings, the service, the atmosphere and the company. Celebrate the fact that you can still appreciate and enjoy places like this whilst maintaining your natural blueprint weight. (Think about all the people who are still slaves to dieting.)

- Take the time to stop during your meal – even if it is for a minute. It doesn't mean that you have to stop eating, but just by stopping and re-connecting with your body, you'll give yourself some time to decide whether you want to stop or continue eating.

- If you have a variety of foods on your plate, then get into the habit of rating your food. I remember school dinners at Primary School where one of the common favourites was fish-fingers, chips and beans. I can remember many of the children gulping down the chips and beans and saving their fish fingers till the end so that they could really savour them. But if only we'd been taught to re-verse this strategy! If instead we had chosen to eat the fish fingers first, then we probably wouldn't have been too bothered about finishing the rest of the food on the plate once we were physically satisfied.

 So the moral of the "fish fingers, chips and beans" story? Eat your favourite foods first and savour each mouthful – and then stop once you're physically satisfied!

Don't Be Too Hard on Yourself

As mentioned before, this may be one of the hardest things that you have to master. I cannot tell you the number of times I have thought this the hardest task, (in fact I did it for four years before I took conscious effort to change it). Please remember to be patient with yourself. This may not be what you want to hear, especially if you are desperate to lose the weight, but I assure you, being easier on yourself will make it easier for you to lose the weight. This concept isn't only about shifting your weight, it's about shifting your mind-set. If you have been in a habit of overeating for a while, it may take time for you to settle with this principle. Even if it means that you can stop just for a minute during your meal and listen to your body, it's a step in the right direction

The Story So Far...

So we've reached the end of the physical aspect of being 'whole' and before we move any further, let's just take a look a summary of the main points:

1. See yourself as being 'whole'.

2. Your natural state is one of well-being.

3. When we eat emotionally, it's a calling that we really need to find out what is really happening within us.

4. Diets don't give you long term success.

5. Not all emotional eaters are the same, so you have to work on becoming an expert on you.

6. Start to make peace with the natural shape of your body.

7. When you are physically hungry, eat.

8. Pay attention when you eat. In other words, show up for your mealtimes.

9. Give yourself permission to eat whatever you want and for many people the food will lose its character. However, remember to be mindful about how the food feels in your body.

10. Stop when you are physically full.

What we have covered so far is very important because it has taught you how to realign with your natural body signals again. However, do not underestimate the power of the following chapters. From personal experience, I have seen some people fall back into their old patterns even though they are familiar with the physical aspects, but I have seen most progress where people give the same importance to addressing the emotional aspect as well as the physical. In fact, some of my clients will tell you that they feel addressing the emotional aspect is far more important.

So, I would like to offer you two pieces of advice for the following chapters. The first is to keep an open mind. The second is to give the process some time. As you didn't develop your habits and patterns overnight, it may take some time to change them.

Here goes...

I AM POWERFUL

I am responsible for what I choose to create in my life.

I have the power to realign with my natural body shape.

I am connected to an infinite Source of well-being and therefore healing my relationship with food is very possible.

I understand that I have the power to separate my emotions from food.

I am always in a position where I can honour my body because the power to make decisions for myself lies within me.

I always have access to an infinite number of choices.

I AM POWERFUL.

8

THE POWER OF EMOTIONS

"Learning to separate food from emotions is a start. But understanding the root of your emotions is the key."

- Sunita Pattani

I believe that to get to the root and heal emotional eating, you've got to look at the bigger picture and come to terms with the possibility that there's more to you that meets the eye. What I am about to share with you may sound a little different, but in my opinion much of what we have been doing so far to heal emotional eating hasn't been working too well. People are still suffering and our relationship with food is still much misunderstood.

I mentioned earlier that addressing the physical aspect (including the nutritional element) alone isn't enough because it is only dealing with the symptom. We need to go deeper than just the symptom and really begin to address the root cause, and in order to do this we need to revisit *The Foundation* that I introduced at the beginning.

In chapter one I outlined the three factors which I feel are the foundation of both forming a healthy relationship with food and realigning with your natural body weight. They are:

1. The need to consider yourself as a 'whole.'

2. Your natural state is one of well-being.

3. The need to eat when we're not hungry is a calling that we need to find out what's really happening within us.

The first thing to take into consideration when considering yourself as a 'whole' is to acknowledge that you are a composite of three factors: Mind, Body and Soul, and that all three of these factors play a role in emotional eating. Mind and Body are probably two factors that most people are familiar with when it comes to emotional eating, but the Soul is most likely the one factor that some people may shy away from because it's not so openly discussed. (Don't get me wrong, my intention for writing this is not to convince you that this element exists, but rather to share with you an alternative idea.)

To be able to consider yourself as a 'whole', there's got to be a level of acknowledgement that you are part of something much bigger and that a positive, life-giving force is flowing through you. It's the same life force that flows through nature and all of life, and I also believe that it is this same force that is responsible for inspiration.

The second foundation talks about our true nature, which I believe is one of love and magnificence, one of wanting to experience freedom and joy. The only issue however is that many of us seem to have forgotten who we really are and instead of striving to connect with that magical feeling again, we take solace in food.

As babies we are still very connected to our natural state of wellbeing. We are totally in love with ourselves, joyous and very forgiving too. We don't worry about our size and neither do we perceive ourselves to be imperfect in any way. The love that we feel for ourselves is us *connecting* with our life-force. We also have our minds, which at this point are like blank slates that have not yet been written on. So the question that we need to be asking is if we were so aligned as babies, how did we become emotional eaters?

The Mind

In order to answer this question, we need to have an understanding of the way in which the mind works. There are some people that I know that buy the most expensive gadgets on the market and have some powerful systems at hand, but the fact of the matter is that these objects are only useful if you know how to use them properly. Your mind is very similar, it's one of the most powerful tools that you have at your disposal. The only problem is that if you don't understand how it works properly, you're unable to use it to your advantage.

To illustrate how the mind works, I would like to share a visual representation with you that was introduced in the 1930s by a medical doctor by the name of Thurman Fleet. Dr. Fleet recognised that in order to treat his patients effectively, he had to give them an image of health to work with. In other words, the patients had to think, see and feel themselves as healthy in order to speed up their recovery process. To help explain this concept, the Doctor developed the

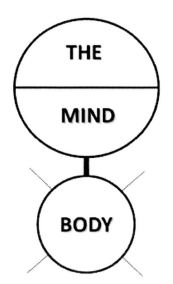

Fig.1 - The Stick Person introduced by Dr. Thurman Fleet,
1934.

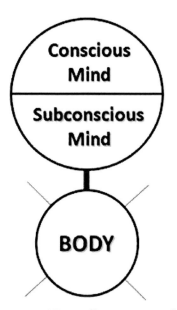

Fig. 2 - The Different Parts of
the Mind

Stick Person Diagram (fig. 1) which shows how
the mind affects the body.

The basic principle behind this diagram is that
your mind causes your body to act in a certain
way, and it's these actions that produce your
results. This is why the diagram illustrates the
mind as being larger than the body, because it
is the mind which is responsible for all manifestations. The body is only a result; it's a mere
manifestation of what is going on in your mind.

The diagram (fig. 2) on the left illustrates that
the mind is split into two parts: the conscious
mind and the subconscious mind.

The Conscious Mind

The conscious mind is your thinking or objec-
tive mind. It allows you to make choices and
learn through observation, education and experience. One of the most important things about
the conscious mind is that it acts as a guardian
over the subconscious mind.

This means that it is responsible for what information filters into your subconscious.

But the question to be asking is, what
influences your conscious mind? What causes
you to think the thoughts that you do? Well,
we have our five physical senses. We have taste,
touch, hearing, smell and sight. Most people
will base their thoughts on information gath-
ered from the outside world using these five
physical senses. This means that as children
we start developing opinions about ourselves
based on what we pick up from the people
around us, and because we don't yet have the
maturity to deal with the information we're
receiving, we believe it to be correct and hence our belief systems begin to form.

The Subconscious Mind

The subconscious element of our mind is more powerful than the conscious part, and is in fact responsible for most of the activity in our daily lives. This part of our mind already has survival instincts etched into it when we are born, and as we begin to grow, our conscious mind starts to develop and picks up messages through our physical senses, which it filters through to the subconscious. Over time our experiences increase and the database grows. This creates our belief system.

The thoughts we think also give rise to emotions which impact our actions. For example, if someone was continually told as a child that they they'll always be overweight because they're from an overweight family, the child may grow up thinking that it's impossible to lose the weight and therefore may not even attempt or entertain the idea of realigning with their natural body shape. In short, our thoughts give rise to our emotions and our emotions drive our actions, which determine the results that we produce.

Noticing Your Belief Patterns

Where weight is concerned, some people gain weight simply because they don't realise that their body is sending them signals all the time. For these people, as soon as they become aware of listening to their bodies again, they find that the weight comes off quite easily. They recognise where they are going wrong, decide to correct it, and move on.

However, for others the journey may not be as easy. Consider this: studies show that up until the age of around seven years old, the child is in a dream-like state, where the mind is like a sponge, absorbing everything about its surroundings. Unfortunately, we don't have any filters in place telling us what is and what isn't appropriate, hence we store every bit of information. Quite often our beliefs about ourselves can be set in place from this early on.

With regards to emotional eating, for some the challenge may have started from childhood. Whereas for others, they may have had a healthy relationship with food up until a certain age, and then decided to diet because their friends were on diets, of course forming more beliefs about food and themselves along the way. The thing to remember however, is that although we are living our lives according to our belief systems, it is possible to change a belief about yourself. It may take time, but it is possible.

The Link

To show you how all this information fits together, I am going to share my own emotional eating journey with you by taking you through a time-line of my life, and explaining how various incidents impacted me:

Age 0-5:

I was born. I don't remember a whole lot, but I do remember either being told, or listening to my parents being told that I was a chubby baby.

The Impact: I was born very connected to who I was – a perfect composite of mind, body and soul. I didn't have any pre-conceived ideas about life or myself, and I happily learned how to walk and talk. I didn't beat myself up over making mistakes. But then at some point, I began making a connection between me and the word 'chubby.' My conscious mind was repeatedly receiving information and filtering it through to my subconscious mind. I was forming the belief that I was 'chubby'.

Age 5-10:

I probably developed a perception of what the term 'fat' meant during this time. I remember thinking that I was chubbier than other girls (although I looking back, I wasn't). I was also taller (ironic really, seen as I am 5'2" tall now). Although I was well nourished in terms of nutrition, I didn't really have the freedom to eat whatever I wanted. I was never allowed to have a whole can of coke or lemonade all to myself and neither was I allowed to finish a whole bar of chocolate (as it was considered greedy).

There is one particular incident that I remember from the age of around six years old. Every Saturday morning, we used to go the Queens Market in Upton Park, and near the entrance there was a bakery that we used to visit. This bakery made the yummiest cherry bread that I had ever tasted, and each week we would buy a loaf. Well, one particular week, we took the bread home and I remember clearly having a slice with our mid-morning tea. After finishing my share, I asked my Dad whether I could have another slice – and, to my disappointment, he said no. Now, as I really wanted that cherry bread, I decided to sneak a piece away whilst clearing the kitchen. I remember cutting the loaf, putting the margarine on, and wolfing it down my throat as fast as I could – half afraid that I would get caught at any moment. Well, I didn't get caught red-handed, but somehow (and to this day I don't know how), my Dad knew that I had eaten some more cherry bread, and of course I got into a lot of trouble.

The Impact: At some point during this time I learned that I had to eat in secret if I wanted to eat whatever I wanted. So each time I would make something to eat, I would always be nibbling through the preparation process. This way nobody would notice that I had eaten. It was quite common for me to eat a three or four pieces of bread whilst making a sandwich.

I would never taste the food; instead I would just shovel it in as quickly as I could. I had stopped honouring my body's natural hunger-satiety signals. I also learned not to trust my own body and associated guilt with a lot of foods. Again, my conscious mind was receiving information and not knowing any better, I chose to think these thoughts and repeat these actions over and over. Lifelong habits were starting to form.

Age 10-18:

This was probably one of the most difficult periods of my life. I hated my body. At age 14, I started to starve myself, followed by binging episodes. Secondary school meant freedom to eat because I had money to spend on food each day, and nobody to tell me what to eat. At this point I had no idea what tasting food was actually about. I couldn't tell whether I was hungry or full and eating for me was on autopilot. And although I wasn't extremely overweight, (probably a size 12-14), I can't remember ever wanting to shop for nice clothes - even though I was always encouraged to. At age 18, I started my first ever 'official' diet. I was encouraged to eat certain 'healthy' foods to my heart's content and became totally obsessed with the scales.

The Impact: I already had beliefs about eating and being overweight. Now that I had been introduced to diets, I started to receive conflicting information about food. Hunger and satiety were not mentioned at all and I started to label foods as being 'good' or 'bad'. Every time I consumed a 'bad' food even in the smallest quantity, I felt really guilty.

Age 18-28:

A lot happened during this phase of my life. I met my husband, had my gall-bladder removed, got married at age 22, qualified as a teacher, tried more diets, went from a size 10 to a size 20, experienced a serious business collapse and my marriage nearly fell apart.

At age 28, my life was a serious mess. I had gained so much weight that doing the housework was a chore. I couldn't bring myself to leave the house and I had literally no social life. Although the weight was never an issue for my husband, we had shut off all family and friends and I would constantly plead with him to just give me a few more months so that I could lose the weight before we started to socialise again.

But it didn't happen. I couldn't stick to a diet or shift the weight. The problem got worse and I felt totally out of control. My whole life was falling apart.

The Overall Impact: The older I got, the more disconnected from my life I became. I kept on planting the same seeds in my conscious mind, which of course filtered straight into my subconscious, further strengthening my belief systems. I had serious conflicting thoughts about food and couldn't eat anything without feeling 'fat'. Having failed at so many diets, I felt like there was no solution for me. I had no idea that it was possible to change a belief system.

The Bottom Line

The bottom line is quite simply this:

At the heart of every emotional eater lies the lack of love for oneself.

We eat emotionally because we have forgotten who we really are. At our very core we are love, joy and magnificence. We are supposed to enjoy life and feel good. But we forget. Instead, not knowing the power of our minds and how to use them effectively, we start to form belief systems that are a contrast to our natural state.

The fact of the matter is that if we loved ourselves enough to believe that we were truly magnificent, we would not feel the need to turn to food. We would have too much respect for ourselves to cause ourselves damage. We would seek to find joy at every opportunity because we would feel worthy of it.

We're not in pain because we're eating emotionally, but instead we eat emotionally because we're in pain. The day you realise that the pain is a result of your own subconscious programming will be the day that you finally begin to set yourself free. When you understand that every negative emotion that you feel about yourself is changeable, you will move towards reconnecting with yourself again. It's not the food you want, it's life.

PUTTING IT INTO PRACTICE

This exercise has been designed to help you identify what belief systems you have in place and what impact they are having on you. The first column is for you to provide your age. In the second column write down what experiences you think may have caused you to become an emotional eater. In the third column write down what belief system you may have formed as a result of those experiences you encountered. An example has been provided for you.

Age range	What you can remember?	The belief system created and how does this relate to food or eating or body image?
0-8 years	I remember being told that I was a 'chubby' child. I also remember having rigid eating times where food was always served up for you. I wasn't allowed to leave the dinner table until I had finished all my food. I was never allowed to answer elders back.	The belief that I was chubby. Had to eat at certain times, regardless of whether I was hungry or not – started to believe that this was the norm. Had to finish everything on my plate. Learned that I wasn't worthy of expressing my opinions.

I AM FORGIVENESS

I understand that forgiveness is one of the most powerful gifts that I can give myself.

When I am able to forgive both myself and others, I begin to release myself from pain.

Nobody has ever achieved anything great by hating themselves.

Today is the day that I work on forgiving myself.

I forgive myself for thinking that I was never good enough.

I forgive myself for not loving myself enough.

I AM FORGIVENESS

9

SETTING YOURSELF FREE

"It's only when you realise that you are the captain of your ship, can you then make a positive change in your life."

– Sunita Pattani

So, by now you should be aware that ultimately your natural state is one of well-being, but through others around you and the inadequate use of your mind, you quickly forget that this is the case. However, there is some part of you on some level that still seeks to reconnect and experience that joy, but because this is not synonymous to what you are experiencing in life, it starts to show up in your experience as the 'void.' In an effort to reduce this uncomfortable feeling (the 'void'), you turn to food which acts as a plaster on the wound – it provides you with a temporary form of relief.

The next step to healing emotional eating is learning how to set yourself free. You've already been given the eating principles in the earlier chapters, but now you need to learn how to fill that void without using food. In order to set yourself free, there are two factors that need to be addressed:

1. YOU

2. LIFE

Realistically speaking the only factor that you ever have control over is you. You are the one that decides how you respond to things and you are also the one who has made the decision to eat emotionally. The reason why I have also listed 'life' as a factor is not because it is something that you have to fix, but rather a factor that you need to learn how to deal with. I am a firm believer that we are co-creators of our own lives through the power of our own thoughts, but I also know we can't always control what life brings our way. For example, no matter how positive we are, we will all still have to face losing a loved one someday and this isn't something that we have control over. It's a part of life. We can however control the way that we respond to these challenges. We can learn how to deal with our emotions.

The Power of Responsibility

For the remainder of this chapter we are going to focus on you and what changes you can implement to heal yourself. The next chapter will look at how to deal with the different emotions that life brings.

One of the most powerful steps to heal emotional eating is taking 100% responsibility for your actions. This means that you realise that you are in your current situation because of certain choices that you have made in the past. The fact of the matter is, that in each moment you have a choice, and the choice that you make determines your life experiences. Taking 100% responsibility is about thinking about the consequences of your actions before you act, and then be willing to take responsibility for the outcome - no matter what happens.

Whether you are a binge eater, a mild emotional eater, a serial dieter, or someone who just can't seem to shift those few extra pounds, the bottom line is that at some point you made a choice to take that route, and the only path to your freedom is if you make a conscious choice to correct the thinking that led to that behaviour.

I had been 'studying' this route for four years before I decided to commit to the responsibility of shifting my shape. I knew everything about 'intuitive eating' that you could possibly know. I'd studied every book on the topic that I could find over and over. The problem was I never quite got around to applying the knowledge that I had learned. It was because I was scared of giving myself freedom with food. I simply didn't believe that I could trust my body, eat what I wanted and still lose weight.

One of the major problems I had once I had decided to heal myself, was that I had convinced myself that diets didn't bring long term success. That bit was fine, but neither did I implement any other approach. The result? Unconditional permission to binge for four years, and sixty pounds of weight gained. Not to mention I was stuck.

If you really want to change, you will need to take this first step of taking responsibility for your actions from now on. If you're not willing to lift the responsibility, you're unlikely to produce the desired results. Make a commitment to adhere to some (or all) of the principles discussed in this book.

The Power of Forgiveness

When some of my clients realise that a large part of them becoming emotional eaters has been to do with their belief systems, they become angry. They start to blame others who are quite often members of their immediate family as they begin to understand that they are products of some-one else's thinking. Some clients even become frustrated with themselves as they wonder how they forgot to listen to their own body and needs.

If you find yourself experiencing similar feelings, stop. Start to notice when you play the blame game and then make a conscious decision to stop. Stop because you didn't realise what you were doing. Stop because those around you didn't know what they were doing and did the best that they could. Stop because you'll never be able to fully move forward if you are carrying around resentment. Yes, there are many factors that relate to why you may have issues with poor body image or weight, but you need to let them go, because you can't bring in something new if you don't first let go of the old. The past is the past and you can't do anything to change it, it's what you do from now on that matters because you have a higher level of awareness.

From this moment on make a decision to expand your awareness, and to learn more about yourself. Come to terms with the fact that on this stage that we call life, you are the main character – the star of the show, and ultimately you are responsible for the decisions that you make, and the experiences that you create. Forgiveness is essential on this path.

What You Think of You Matters – The Self-Image

Your self-image is the hidden image that controls what you think is possible for you, and has developed through the thoughts and feelings that you have continually thought and felt about yourself. It is what determines your self-worth. In fact it is your self-image that controls the results in every aspect of your life. Many people who have suffered from emotional eating have a poor self-image and they simply do not consider themselves worthy enough to treat themselves with respect.

It is worth remembering that your self-image didn't form overnight and hence it may take some time to change. For example, if you've always felt overweight and ashamed of your body, it's unlikely you will feel brilliant about yourself straight away. For most people it's a step-by-step process where they begin to feel better about themselves over time.

The thing to take on board about improving your self-image is that you need to move at a pace that is comfortable for you. It doesn't matter what others think you should be doing, all that matters is how *you feel about what you're doing*. Let me share an example with you.

Prior to establishing a healthy relationship with food, I probably spent most of my life living with a very poor self-image. It didn't really matter to me that I was a qualified teacher and that academically I had achieved a lot, it didn't mean anything to me when people told me I was beautiful. Even when I had managed to 'mould myself' slim by endless starving or unhealthy dieting, I still felt as if I didn't look good in the clothes and shopping would be an absolute nightmare (even when I was a size 10).

Due to the fact that as a child I was constantly told that I was chubby, I had learned to hide my body away, and not be proud or grateful for it. And because I was already aware and conscious of my weight from a very young age, my goal and aspiration became to look like the models and actresses on television and in magazines. Their shape seemed perfect to me and I felt that that is what I should have looked like. It didn't occur to me at that age that perhaps my natural body shape was different from theirs. I just thought that if I lost the weight, I would start to look like them.

As I got older, I realised that maybe I would never get to be that shape and maybe I was not good enough. And it didn't matter how slim I became, I would still feel overweight. My childhood programming was dictating my adult responses and I didn't even know it was happening.

During my lowest point, I would live in jogging bottoms and sweatshirts. And although it's still very difficult for me to admit (I thought very carefully about adding the following sentence), I had two pairs of joggers and three tops which I would rotate, carefully, planning when to wash the clothes so that I always had something fresh to wear. No variety. No different colours. No make-up. No leaving the house – unless it was essential (in which case, I would go shopping where there would be a minimal chance of bumping into somebody that I knew). That was my life.

People would continually tell me to make more of an effort. Some family members just couldn't understand what I was going through. On the odd occasion, I would decide that I would go shopping and buy some nice clothes, and try and take care of myself. But, the change would never last; because not only had I always felt fat in clothes, but every time I had tried to do this, it reminded me of how much weight I had actually gained. A task which had been excruciatingly painful when I was slim, became unbearable with the addition of extra weight. It was a cycle I just couldn't seem to fix. Then, one of my family members would come by for the umpteenth time and say that famous line, *"you're still wearing those dirty old clothes. Can't you wear anything different?"* I can't tell you how painful it was to have to listen to that on almost a daily basis.

So, what happened? Where did it all change? Well, when I first decided that I wanted to seriously try and heal my relationship with food, I felt it would be too much changing everything all at once. I didn't think I could deal with my eating as well as changing my image all at the same time, especially since I had gained so much weight. The pressure was too much. So, I decided that I would start solely by focusing on the eating and listening carefully to my body's signals. I completely switched off to my clothing and turned a blind eye to it.

Even though I would stumble with the eating (it took me a while before I could follow my body's natural signals), I realised that I was making some progress. I was no longer bingeing every day. When I got to this point, I remember thinking that I wanted to be kinder to my body, and although I still wasn't ready to expand my wardrobe, I slowly started to take some time out to paint may nails. Shortly after, I bought a facial mask and body scrubs and lotions that smelt delicious. Slowly, I started to look forward to my weekly pamper session which would be all about me. The more I treated my body kindly, the more I wanted to treat my body kindly. And then, one day I woke up and felt that I was no longer comfortable in my joggers, I wanted to go out and experiment with some clothes.

The first shopping trip was an absolute disaster. I couldn't fit into a pair of trousers, so I left the shop feeling disheartened, and came home. However, with continual persistence, I eventually found five tops that I was comfortable in and two pairs of trousers. It may have been slow, but it was a great start.

When I sat down to evaluate what had changed, I realised that for the first time in my life, the change had come from within. Instead of going out there and buying new clothes to wear straight away, I did what was comfortable for me. The change had actually happened backwards. I had changed the way *I felt about my body* and that somehow changed the outer manifestation. Was it easy? Not all of it. But with persistence, I did get there in the end.

I don't know whether your story is similar to mine, perhaps you may be starting off in a better place? Wherever you are along this journey, one of the most valuable pieces of advice that I can offer you is **do what feels right for you**. Having worked with a number of clients, I have come to learn that nobody achieves anything great from a standpoint of not feeling good about themselves. If you find that buying new clothes feels like a daunting experience, then start small. The last thing you want is to be feeling disheartened and self-conscious about yourself, and turning to food. This is a journey of self-love not a marathon to breaking free from emotional eating. I can't stress this enough. At the end of the day, this is your journey. Even if others have had a similar experience to yours, the way you handle things may be different. Nobody can really tell you what to do because nobody (apart from you), knows exactly what you are going through.

In order to change your self-image, you've got to start changing the way that you think and feel about yourself. It is about realising and accepting that your opinion of yourself so far isn't an accurate reflection of who you really are. I have said it before and I will say it again: *you are magnificent and you absolutely deserve to love yourself.*

PUTTING IT INTO PRACTICE

1. **The negative beliefs that you hold about yourself are not true.**

   Remember that change begins from within. Having a poor self-image comes from you having programmed your mind with false information about yourself. You have developed ideas and opinions about yourself based on your past experiences. It is worth remembering that each moment can be a new beginning if that's what you want. In order to change, you will have to start to show your body some love and respect. It may not be easy at first, but it does get easier.

2. **Observe your self-talk.**

   Start to treat your body with respect. Listen to the way you talk to yourself. If you constantly criticise yourself, how do you think your body will respond? Would you accept it if someone was hurling abuse at you on the street? Probably not. Most people will demand a certain level of respect from others. If this is the case, why do you treat yourself with any less respect? It's also important to remember that your subconscious mind has no sense of humour, so whatever thought you choose to think, your subconscious mind will believe and hence have you act in that way.

   The idea is to start feeling good about yourself. This journey is all about 'feeling' your way to your natural body shape. Now, here's the thing: if you have been in a place where you have felt very negatively about yourself, then it's going to be very difficult for you to suddenly start believing something very positive about yourself. For example, if you try to say to yourself, "I love my beautiful body," but in reality are feeling fat and useless, those positive words alone will have no impact on the way you feel because you simply will not believe them.

   A better technique to use is to start where you feel comfortable. What do you appreciate about yourself or your body? If you can't find anything external that you like, then focus on the internal functions. Do you appreciate the fact that you have lungs to breathe in fresh air? What about a well-functioning heart or kidneys? Maybe you are somebody who has a real talent in music or art? What aspect of yourself do you really appreciate?

Once you have found a few features that you are comfortable with, use them to construct affirmations. Affirmations are positive statements about yourself that you make to yourself. Affirmations are also stated in the present tense. Here are some examples:

"I am grateful that I have healthy lungs."

"I like the colour of my eyes."

"I am grateful to have legs that enable me to walk."

"I like my smile."

"I am academically very intelligent."

"I am beginning to appreciate my curves."

"I can trust myself to feed me appropriately"

"I am good at my job"

"I enjoy feeding my body healthy foods."

The main aim here is that the affirmations *make you feel good* because when you appreciate and feel good about yourself, it is reflected in your actions. As you begin to feel good about yourself, you will find it easier to appreciate other positive aspects of yourself. In other words: when you feel good, it just keeps on getting better!

Try to think of your body as a child. If you are kind and loving towards a child, you will receive a kind and loving response. Loving your body works in exactly the same way. In fact, I was amazed at how easy it was to lose the weight once I started loving and accepting my body. It was such a contrast to the previous negative self-talk and restrictive eating that I had engaged in, that it literally felt as if I had released a struggle. I also noticed that because I did appreciate my body, I thought twice about what I was putting into it.

3.   **Don't be afraid to start small.**

If you are finding that your self-image is really poor, and has been hold-ing you back significantly, then start small. Don't feel as if you have to do everything all at once. What is the smallest thing that you could do comfortably that will start to show your body that you love and care for it? Remember, this journey is all about you. Nobody else knows what you have been, or are going through. Do what feels right for you. Take a look at some of the suggestions below.

- Start to focus on the parts of the body that you do like. For example, are your eyes a beautiful deep colour? Or perhaps your hands and feet are elegant? Is your hair thick and luscious, or fine and easy to style? Have you got a wonderful smile? If you are finding it difficult to find any positive features, ask someone close to you to name a few. Quite often we do not see in ourselves what other people class to be the beauty in us.

- Perhaps schedule in a weekly pamper session for yourself. This doesn't have to be expensive, it could just be in the comfort of your of your own home. Treat your body to some delicious scrubs and lotions. You could even ask a friend or a family member to come and join you; perhaps you can give each other a mini-facial or a manicure.

- Take some time out when you can and have a soak in the bath. Use this time to relax all your muscles and relieve the tension from your body. You may want to light some candles to help you relax.

- Take some time out (daily if you can), to be alone. You may want to light some incense sticks, candles or an oil burner to set the mood. Try and just sit silently observing your thoughts and emo-tions. (This doesn't have to take long; even 10 minutes will have an effect). There are some excellent guided meditations available to help you relax, which you can purchase from your local book-store or over the internet.

- If you like make-up, wear some on a daily basis. Even if you feel you are not ready to step out of your 'comfort clothes', just put on a bit of mascara or lipstick, or whatever else you fancy! Remember that every step, no matter how small is a step in the right direc-tion.

- Get your hair cut or styled – have the hairdressing salon pamper you!

- Taking a daily walk can also do you wonders. Apart from the obvious physical benefits, it can be a fantastic time for you to clear your head and be out appreciating the fresh air. I personally love listening to music whilst out walking and I always come back feeling fresh and invigorated. If you choose to go for a walk with a friend, it can also be a great opportunity to catch up!

4. **Take out 15 minutes a day to factor in some visualisation.**

One of the most amazing features of the mind is that it can't tell the different between what's real and what's imagined. This means that if you focus on a thought long enough to evoke a feeling, your subconscious mind will have you behave in a way that will manifest different results.

Many of the people that I come across don't realise the power of visualisation, and although the focus of this book is emotional eating, I feel that you need to be aware of the possibility that there might be something deeper driving the results that you have been creating for yourself so far. It is not my intention to fully explain the science behind visualisation, but it is my intention to put forward the importance of visualisation and what benefits it may be able to bring forth for you.

In her book 'The Field', Lynn McTaggart brings to light some amazing discoveries that she came across as a result of eight years research with some of the top-graded scientists. She presents the idea that the *consciousness of an observer brings an observed object into being. Nothing in the universe exists as an 'actual thing' independently of our perception to it.* This means that every minute of every day, we are creating our own reality[14]. So what does this mean for you? It means that whatever you are thinking about is what you are creating for yourself. You are the creator of your own experience. If you choose to think and feel fat, you are creating a self-fulfilling prophecy and will further bring that manifestation into your experience. Going back to the topic of diets, this is why they fail to work as a long-term solution, because you're only fixing the food, not the thinking.

The question now is, how can you use this information to help yourself? I would suggest that you start to imagine what it would be

14 Reprinted by permission of Harper Collins Publishers Ltd © 2003 Lynne McTaggart.

like to be free from emotional eating. What impact would it have on the shape of your body? What food choices would you make? What clothes would you choose to wear? How would your life change? Write down a new story about yourself as you would like yourself to be and then make a recording of it. Listen to this recording every day and really try to feel what it would feel like to have this manifest in your life. If you feel that you don't resonate with making a recording, then alternatively you could just take out fifteen minutes each day, close your eyes and visualise. The aim of this activity is to dream with joyful emotion. You'll be surprised at what choices you will start to make once you are in a happier place.

I AM ALL-EMBRACING

I understand that experiencing discomfort is a natural part of life and I now have the tools to be able to deal with it.

I understand that discomfort is cyclical – nothing lasts forever.

Life is always conspiring wellness. Even within the darkest moments, there is a ray of light, an opportunity for my growth.

I accept that everyone is different and that this brings colour to life.

It is ok for me to feel all emotions.

I AM ALL- EMBRACING

10

FEELING THE DISCOMFORT

*" Separating your emotions from food means that you will have to face up to
the discomfort. If you feel unhappy, allow yourself to be unhappy, because no
amount of food can ever be a permanent plaster."*

- Sunita Pattani

In the last chapter I mentioned that there were two factors that needed to be addressed to set yourself free. The first factor was YOU and we have already discussed some strategies as to how you can implement forgiveness and improve your self-image. The second factor was LIFE and I mentioned that you can't always control what life brings your way, but you can control the way in which you choose to respond to it.

The Difference between Responding and Reacting

There is a big difference between responding and reacting. Most people react to situations. This means that they do not give much thought to their responses. For example, an emotional eater may experience an uncomfortable situation and react by turning to food.

Responding on the other hand, requires a higher level of awareness. It asks that you think about your response before responding. The little gap that is created between the situation and your perception of the situation is the only place where you can make a difference. For example, an emotional eater who is in the midst of experiencing an uncomfortable situation may choose to just stop and reflect for 30 seconds. This time gives them the opportunity to evaluate the situation and decide on a response. In other words, it brings a level of consciousness to the situation.

Dealing with life is not about life itself, it's about dealing with your perception of life. In the last chapter I introduced you to the idea that what you create in your life comes down to the thoughts and feelings that you choose to experience. If you choose to feel and focus upon negative feelings most of the time, this is what you will draw into your experience. However, this doesn't mean that you have to become obsessive about feeling good all the time, because this in itself can be an added pressure for some people, which defeats the whole object of feeling good in the first place.

So here's the thing: we know that our thoughts and feelings create our reality, but we also know that life isn't a bed of roses all the time. This means that we have to find a way of creating balance and releasing resistance to negative experiences. As we are all likely to experience things in life which we perceive to be negative, we need to work on changing our perception so that we can deal with the situation instead of turning to food.

All the suggestions provided in this chapter are intended to help you deal with uncomfortable feelings. The idea is not that you dwell upon these feelings, but rather to find a safe way of letting them go. Remember our aim is always to be moving in the direction of feeling good as this is our natural state of wellbeing.

Noticing Discomfort

It took me a long time to realise that a lot of the time I was overeating because I was experiencing emotional discomfort. In fact I was so used to the feeling, that for most of my life I didn't even realise that I was suffering emotional discomfort. To me, apart from feeling fat, everything in life was fine.

However, I couldn't understand why I had started to binge so often especially when I came to a point where I was binging every single day. I was suffering, my marriage was suffering, my career was suffering. But still, each day, at around 4pm, the binge would start. Sometimes I wondered whether I had been possessed by a food demon. I couldn't just stop eating. My health was seriously deteriorating. I had become very unfit, my lower back was hurting all the time. My ankles were swollen and I wouldn't leave the house. Waking up each day and living was a chore, because each day I expected the binge. And still I continued to try and fix the food, not deal with my emotions.

Then, one morning I woke up and I knew that things had to change because I knew that I was slowly killing myself. I only had two choices: go on a diet, or establish a normal, healthy relationship with food. (Starving myself probably would have been an option, but I simply did not have the strength to take this route anymore.)

Going on a diet was certainly not an option. Ever since I had discovered intuitive eating, a massive shift had occurred in my consciousness. I knew that diets did not work, but I was also unable to successfully eat 'intuitively'. I felt stuck between two worlds of eating. The only option I had left was to take complete responsibility for my actions, take small steps towards loving myself, and hope for the best. Although I was terrified of taking this step, I decided that I would allow myself to eat anything I wanted when I was hungry, and stop when I felt satisfied. And so my journey began.

During the first few months I made amazing progress, my eating seemed to be stabilising, I was losing weight and I was taking steps on a daily basis to be kind to myself. I remember thinking that this was actually quite easy and I was sure that I would be healed very quickly. But then, one day, very unexpectedly, it happened. I got the urge to binge. It was a very strong urge and I felt as if I just couldn't stop myself. Eventually I gave into the feeling.

The overeating continued for a few days and I could feel those old emotions of worthlessness rising again. I felt guilty at the fact that I was sabotaging my efforts. I worried that I would regain the weight and end up really out of control again. After a few days of this consistent worrying, I somehow got the strength to face what was going on. I sat down to reflect upon what was happening. I was sure that there had to be a reason as to why I felt compelled to overeat again. After much reflection, reading through my journal and searching, I found the answer.

I realised that a few days before the bingeing had started, I had received an upsetting email from a friend of mine. He was writing in response to a message that I had sent him regarding the work I was doing and the progress that I was making with my relationship with food. He wrote back with some pointers on how to lose the weight, and told me that I shouldn't really be spending too much time developing this concept. Although a part of me knew that he was trying to be helpful, I couldn't help but feel a little patronised. I was angry at the fact that firstly, he didn't understand the importance of the work I was doing and secondly he didn't acknowledge my passion and interest about this topic. I felt totally gutted that someone was telling me not to work on something that I loved. I wasn't on this path solely to make money, I was writing because it was helping me to understand what was going on inside of me. How could I explain to him that this was the most inspired time of my life so far?[15] How could I explain to him that I was feeling freer than I had ever felt before? For once, life

---

15 And has continued to be since.

was not about making money or wanting to be thin, life was about learning to respect myself, love myself and establishing a good relationship with food. How could I make him understand that there was now a light at the end of the tunnel for me? If there was a light at the end of the tunnel for me, a chronic dieter and compulsive eater, that meant that there was light at the end of the tunnel for others too. It meant that there was a way for people to end both their dieting episodes, and their suffering.

I was surprised at the fact that I had felt all this discomfort, and I had not acknowledged it properly. You see, *I was strong* and I didn't let things like this get in my way. I didn't like allowing myself to disagree with other people. I liked to keep people happy because I was terrified of upsetting them. So, instead of speaking my mind, I wanted food. I wanted to stuff my emotions down by eating. I didn't want to feel the pain of these uncomfortable emotions, I wanted to be numb, where nothing or no-one could affect me. And of course, the only way that I was able to deal with this was by eating.

As soon as I acknowledged what was going on, all of a sudden bingeing was not something that I felt guilty over, it was an indication that I wasn't dealing with life appropriately. I understood at this point that I had two options. I could tiptoe through life just hoping that nothing too harsh was tossed my way. If I did encounter something difficult, it wouldn't matter because I could just eat. However, all this would be at the cost of me not living my life to its fullest. The second option would be to face up to the pain. Experience the pain. Embrace the pain. This also meant that sometimes the pain may be difficult to bear, and food may have to step in to play the part of the plaster. Was I willing to put up with that? Yes. It seemed a better choice. It didn't mean that the binges would definitely disappear, it meant that I was willing to get to know myself better.

As soon as I started to acknowledge my emotions and my discomfort, I realised that sometimes I felt claustrophobic. Sometimes the discomfort would be dull – an ache (not necessarily physical), and sometimes it would be sharp, unbearable and angry. There were times when the pain would be physical, such as a headache, and rather than eating I would choose to have a quick nap or a relaxing hot bath. I started writing a lot in my journal as well to help me make sense of what I was feeling. I also took the time to experience the emotions, and soon I realised that I was using food less and less to deal with the pain.

The fact of the matter is that everyone experiences discomfort at some point during their life. People feel discomfort when they are faced by people they dislike, when they get poor grades at school, when their children are hurt, when they can't eat the food they want, when the mother-in-law is coming to stay, when the spouse doesn't listen, when they lose their job, when they witness betrayal etc. My point is, discomfort is part of life and not dealing with this feeling (or any sort of negative feeling) can lead to other emotional outlets, such as overeating. Now when I look back, I realise that I was eating uncontrollably because food was the only thing that would not 'talk' back to me. It had no emotion, it had no judgement. And because I felt as if I had no control over my emotions, no way to control my discomfort, I found something that I felt I had control over, which was food. I know it sounds like a bit of a paradox, but the only thing I felt that I had control over was food and yet I was eating it uncontrollably.

PUTTING IT INTO PRACTICE

Here are some suggestions to help you deal with emotions:

- **Understand that emotions are a natural part of life, and know it's ok to feel them:**

  Discomfort, pain, anger, jealously, love, kindness, joy and all other emotions are a part of life, and you will encounter them at some point. Generally, human beings do not like the feeling of discomfort, and many of us would rather eat, drink, smoke etc. through the pain. However, if we want to re-claim our perfect body, we need to separate our emotions from food. Now, I am not suggesting that you stop feeling the joy of eating. Food is a pleasure that should be enjoyed. I am talking about the rest of life.

  Many people who overeat link food and emotions together, which means that you may be eating because you are feeling a particular emotion. Separating food from emotion means that you are eating to live, you are eating because you have to nourish yourself and because your body needs fuel. Separating food from emotions also means that you are acknowledging that emotions are emotions. You need to feel and deal with the emotions without using food as a plaster.

  In order to feel the emotion, any time you encounter discomfort, take a few minutes to acknowledge it. Close your eyes and focus on the sensations within your body. Where can you feel the tension? What does it look like to you? Can you give it name? Just allow yourself to feel it. For example, if you are feeling upset about something, rather than carrying that energy, allow yourself to cry if you need to and get it out of your system. Spend some time, even if it's just five minutes connecting to the way that you feel. I will add a caution here though. Remember that the point is not to dwell on the feeling for too long. The aim is to feel the feeling and let it go so that you release any resistance that you may be feeling.

  Also it's very important at this point to acknowledge the fact that no amount of food is going to fix what's really going on, and at that point you have a choice: to honour yourself and your emotions by not eating, and dealing with the pain instead; or to go ahead and use food to numb yourself.

You may find that when you do separate food from emotions, it may be uncomfortable because if you're not eating to numb the pain, the pain will be there fully present. Also realise that there will be times when you may well choose to overeat because it's too much to bear. Reclaiming your perfect body is not about being rigid and getting it 100% right. Reclaiming your perfect body is about learning to love and respect yourself. It's about being gentle with yourself. It's about understanding that it's ok to forgive yourself when you make mistakes. It may take a while to get comfortable with this, but one step at a time is all it takes.

- **Acknowledge that discomfort does not last forever, it does disappear:**

One of the fundamental laws of life is the law of rhythm. Everything has a natural rhythm: night and day, up and down, tide-in, tide-out. Everything flows. Our natural environment, I feel, has the answer to many questions that we may have on a deeper level. And yet, in our pursuit for success, wealth, achievement etc., we sometimes miss the amazing gift that surrounds us.

Flowers seem to grow effortlessly. They flow through their natural life cycle. No resistance, no fuss, they seem to be in harmony with their existence. They fulfil their role beautifully and then they move on. Trees are the same; they shed their leaves and blossom again throughout their preferred seasons. Nature seems to fulfil its purpose effortlessly. In fact, I believe in its most natural state, the Earth provides enough of everything for everyone. There is natural balance

The point that I am trying to get across, is that even nature exists in cycles – nature grows and nature dies. It's the same with life circumstances. The feeling of discomfort also has a rhythm. It doesn't last forever. It will come and go. And that's really the reassuring part: it will disappear. The issue is not the eating, it's how you deal with the discomfort, which brings me on to the next point:

- **Write your feelings down in a journal, feel and describe your discomfort:**

I first read about the benefits of journaling when I was at University. I knew back then that I had an unhealthy relationship with food and I remember starting a journal. The only problem was I didn't quite understand what I was supposed to write in the journal. It wasn't until quite a few years later that I realised that journaling not only was an excellent tool for emotional release, but also a tool for me to track my eating habits.

Since I had always been the sort of person that liked to keep the peace, and keep other people happy, I hardly ever expressed my true feelings, or voiced my opinion. Funnily enough, I didn't even realise that I was holding on to so much emotion. Journaling highlighted two very important points to me: the first was that I needed to stop playing the 'poor me' game. My underlying belief about myself was that I was never allowed to voice my opinion, and on the odd occasion that I did, nobody would listen. The truth however, was different. I chose not to voice my opinion because I was scared of upsetting people, and I didn't think that my opinion was good enough to be taken seriously. As a result, there was so much emotional build-up within me that I would eat. I was simply not taking responsibility for myself. I had to change my belief system, I had to start believing in myself and learn how to voice my opinion diplomatically.

The second important point that journaling highlighted was that I started to understand the mind-set that was holding me back from releasing the weight. I was an all-or-nothing person, a classic black-and-white thinker. By becoming aware of these two factors, I was able to make progress by taking each day at a time. Each time I would feel the need the need to binge, I would ask myself what was really going on.

When you do experience some discomfort, try writing your feelings down in a journal. For some people, this is an excellent method of releasing some tension, and clarifying thoughts and feelings. Journaling will really give you an insight in to what is going on within. In addition to helping you emotionally, journaling will also help you identify patterns in overeating, what the cause may be, and also which foods seem not to suit you.

For many people, when they first start this journey of self-discovery, they are often unaware of what is causing them to overeat. As they begin to journal, they start to see and reflect upon what is going on within.

Once they understand what is going on, they can then decide how best to tackle the challenge. You becoming an expert on 'you' is really the key to unlocking you natural body weight.

If you find writing uncomfortable, you may want to think about recording your feelings onto a recording device, or perhaps even booking a few one-on-one sessions with me so that we can begin to work through your feelings.

- **Know it's ok to have a good cry, or ask for a hug when you feel the need:**

Many of you may be in the habit of turning to food when you experience discomfort. If this is what you do, take some time out to ask yourself what it is that you really want. What are you feeling discomfort about? What can you give yourself to nurture yourself? Also start to look at the food that you are feeling drawn to eat, why do you think this is?

For example, during one of our personal sessions, one of my clients was concerned because she found that she was often craving hot apple pie and custard, and even though she was trying hard not to give into the temptation, somehow she always managed to persuade herself to eat it, even if she wasn't hungry. When I asked her what she liked about the apple-pie and custard, she said she liked the warmth and sweetness of the food, it made her feel comforted and reminded her of her happy childhood. This particular client was using the food to bring back the happy, safe feeling of being comforted and safe. She was also using it to add sweetness to her life, which she seemed to lack. After talking through her feelings and experiences, she started to see why she was so drawn to this food. She had to find other ways of feeling safe and comforted, and also had to work to bring more sweetness (without the food) into her life.

When I decided that I wanted to change my relationship with food, I realised that sometimes I felt lonely or insecure and I didn't like the feeling because it made me feel uncomfortable. Then, when I managed to pluck up the courage, I started asking for a hug or some 'me' time. Yes, it certainly felt different asking for these things, and to begin with, my body missed the food. But slowly, it became easier to ask for what I really wanted and the more I did it, the less I wanted to use food. Eventually, food became food and was used for the correct reasons (most of the time). And my feelings and needs were looked after in other ways. I started treating myself like a child, honouring myself, nurturing myself and respecting myself.

If I were to offer one valuable piece of information to conclude this chapter, it would be: embrace the discomfort and learn to deal with it, because it is guaranteed to show up in your life.

I AM BALANCED

I choose to bring more balance into my life.

I make choices that nourish me in every way.

I am looking forward to experiencing life in a new light, where my journey is not one of perfection, but rather one of progression.

I understand that balanced thinking will lead to balanced actions.

I understand the power of balance.

I AM BALANCED

11

BREAKING FREE FROM BLACK & WHITE THINKING

*"As long as you are 'on a diet', you always run the risk of being 'off a diet'.
Overeating and starving can be seen as two sides of the same coin. Both are a
manifestation of feeling out of control. It's balance that we really seek."*

– Sunita Pattani

So far we covered *how to eat, the root of emotional eating, how to improve
your self-image and how to deal with discomfort*. In this chapter I am now going to explore one of the major contributors that keeps you locked in the cycle
of emotional eating. This factor is *Black-and-white* thinking, which for many
people acts as an invisible prison that they are unable to break free from.

At the beginning of this book I mentioned that the way in which we eat is a
direct reflection of the way in which we live our lives. For example if we are very
restrictive in the way that we eat, the likelihood is that we are very restrictive in
the way that we live life.

Sue, one of my clients would keep a very close eye on the type and the
amount of food that she was allowing herself to eat. When we looked at how
she lived in life general, we found that there were similar patterns coming
through. Sue had always been a high achiever and had extremely high expectations of herself and her family. One of her main issues however, was that every
few weeks when everyone else was out of the house, she would feel compelled
to consume large amounts of food.

After a few personal sessions, Sue realised that she was being too hard
on herself as she was always striving for perfection. Her need to overeat was a
signal that she had to incorporate more balance into her life.

What is Balance?

One of the main reasons that people struggle with emotional eating is because they fail to understand the power of balance. Achieving balance where eating is concerned is actually a matter for the mind. The primary issue isn't that you balance your episodes of under-eating and overeating, or that you have to carefully balance your intake of carbohydrates, proteins and fat. The primary issue is that you try and strive for something unrealistic, which is 'perfection' and this is what you need to balance.

In order to bring more balance into both your life and your relationship with food, you need to make peace with the fact that it is ok to 'let things go' sometimes. Even naturally slim people occasionally overeat during the time of festivities. The only difference with them is that firstly, they don't go on a 'mad eating frenzy'. They enjoy their food and savour all the different flavours. Secondly, they don't dwell on it. As soon as festivities are over, they don't beat themselves up over their eating, but rather they simply resume their normal eating habits again.

What Does Achieving Balance Look like?

For the remainder of this chapter, I am going to discuss the different levels of thinking that you may experience as you start to introduce more balance into your life. The main message this book is trying to convey is that in order to achieve your natural body weight, you have to listen to your body very carefully and respond accordingly. Your body is forever talking to you and telling you exactly what it needs. The skill that you really need to develop to be able to work in partnership with your body is to **get your mind out of the way when you eat!**

The Intuitive Response Model

Take a look at the diagram below which shows the 'Intuitive Response Model'. The model illustrates the three stages of thinking that you are likely to experience as you move through this journey. Most emotional eaters will start at stage one and then progressively move up to stage three. However, it is important to realise that the progression is not always 'clean cut'. For example, just because you may have reached stage two doesn't mean that you will never experience stage one again. The progression of the stages may not be as simple because it takes time to form new habits.

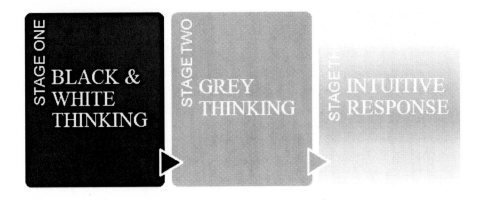

Figure 1 The Intuitive Response Model

There may be some people that move directly from stage one to stage three. These are the people who will take the principles from this book and manage to apply them fairly easily because they may only have a mild emotional attachment to food.

However, if you have experienced quite a turbulent relationship with food, or engage very strongly in black-and-white thinking, then you may find that you will experience all three levels on the way to achieving your natural weight. So, let's take a look at these stages in more detail.

Stage One - Black & White Thinking

Black and white thinking is when you see the world only in extremes, with no middle ground. With regards to eating, this kind of thinking will continue to keep you trapped in a cycle of dieting and overeating. Geneen Roth, often states in her books that for every diet there is an equal and opposite binge, and this makes complete sense seen as we live in a universe of polar opposites. For example, up and down, in and out, black and white, yes and no, diet and binge... get the drift?

One of the main reasons that so many diets fail is because they encourage black and white thinking, which people just cannot adhere to in the long-term. Being 'on a diet' implies that you can also be 'off a diet', therefore you will be stuck in a cycle of having 'good days' followed by 'bad days'. On 'bad days' of course, some people usually give themselves unconditional permission to eat whatever they want in whichever quantities they want because tomorrow is a new day. Tomorrow we will start the diet again.

One of my biggest motivational factors for embarking upon this journey has been watching elderly ladies still struggle with their weight. I know a
seventy-five year old lady who still diets. When I first consciously noticed her
eating behaviour, I realised straight away that I simply could not imagine living
the rest of my life on a diet.

All my life I have watched her overeating on the weekends and on 'special
occasions', quite often until she finds it difficult to breathe. She then lives on
restricted tasteless 'healthy' food throughout the week. This is a typical display
of black & white thinking. Remember what I said earlier? For every diet there is
an equal and opposite binge.

Food is supposed to be a pleasure to be enjoyed, and all foods are acceptable. Many people feel that they don't trust themselves enough to eat whatever
they want and they feel that if they do not have rules in place, they will simply
be out of control where eating is concerned. However, if you do decide to rise
to the challenge of this journey, you will soon come to realise that this is not the
case.

The reason why it is very difficult (and exhausting) to live a life of just
'black' or just 'white' thinking is that at some point, you are going to have to live
a balance between the two. You can't stay on a diet for the rest of your life, (if
we could, we would not have obesity issues and you would have no cause for
reading this book). You need to consider that there will be circumstances when
you will not be able to uphold your 'diet' eating patterns. What happens when
you are on the time of the month, or when you're at a party, or when you've
been invited out to eat, or even during festive celebrations or your birthday?
Even if you do give yourself permission to eat a particular food, chances are you
probably won't enjoy it because you'll be too busy worrying about which part of
your body that food is going to stick to.

I think it is quite important that you learn to balance your eating habits if
you're going to make any progress. I have met many women, (including myself) who were miserable when they were on a diet because everything was
based around food and deprivation a lot of the time. Dieting took the fun out
of everyday life. I know in my case, the balancing act has been paramount to
my recovery as I was (and still am sometimes), a very logical thinker, along with
being quite a perfectionist.

The challenge was that I wouldn't allow myself to 'slip-up'. In fact, my eating pattern was so bad that I even tried to categorize when I was full exactly, but quite often I would have one too many bites – just one, and everything would be ruined, which meant that I now had unconditional permission to binge for the rest of the day. Of course, the whole thing would start again tomorrow. So if you're experiencing something similar, how can you stop the cycle?

Let go of the 'perfectionist' within. You don't have boxes to fill in your stomach; there isn't a perfect distinction between the levels on the hunger scale. The hunger scale is to help you get back in touch with your bodily signals again, but it is not a tool for perfection. It took me a while to know where I was on the hunger scale, and it took me time to get into the habit of feeding my body what it wanted. But, it's also worth pointing out that I made way more progress even with these minor mishaps, than I ever did when I took a 'perfectionist's' attitude. It wasn't necessarily the easiest thing to do, but it got better with time.

Be kind to your body. Pay special attention to it, giving it much positive thought and self-talk, and you'll be amazed at how quickly your body responds. Think of your body as child. When you treat a child disrespectfully, you have trouble gaining the child's love and trust. The child doesn't work in harmony with you. However, when you're kind to that child, he or she will respect you and work with you. It's the same analogy with your body. If you're kind to it and trust it to look after you, it will work in harmony with you – both you and your body need to be playing for the same team. Remember how many amazing things your body already does for you, and learn to trust it to give you accurate hunger-satiety signals. Your body knows how to balance itself out.

Do something different on a regular basis. Many black and white thinkers do not want to move past their comfort zones and hence keep strengthening the same black and white pattern of thought. For example, my client Hayley had been trained since childhood to wash the dishes and put them away straight after the family had finished their meal. As Hayley grew older and had a family of her own, she found herself getting very stressed out because her children refused to follow in her footsteps. Although the children didn't refuse to help out, *they wanted to do their chores* when they wanted to do their chores, which often meant a few hours after dinner had finished. With time, Hayley accepted that it didn't matter if things weren't done to perfection. As a result her relationship with both food and her family improved and she began to embrace spontaneity.

Start to observe what black and white thinking patterns you have and then make the effort to try something new. Try out a new restaurant, park your car in a different place, do something creative that you enjoyed doing as a child, such as painting or wear your 'special occasion' clothes on a 'normal day'. The aim of this activity is to help you make peace with the fact that you don't have to be perfect in life and that the world won't fall apart if you enjoyed your own birthday cake once a year. Life is supposed to be balanced and enjoyable.

Stage 2 – Grey Thinking

In a vast majority of cases, once a person has identified and started to address black-and-white thinking, they usually shift into the grey thinking mode. You may find that this starts to happen when you give yourself full permission to eat whatever you want. At this point you have started to move away from the idea that certain foods are good or bad, and you are prepared to experiment with a variety of foods, some of which perhaps you may not have allowed yourself to eat for years. Although everyone's personal experiences will be different (depending on the beliefs that you have constructed around food), many people find that they go through phases of eating a particular food. For example, you may go through a phase where you eat sausage and mash regularly. Once you have been both psychologically and physiologically satisfied with this combination, you may find that you move on to another food which you have deprived yourself of during the years.

For many people, this is an essential level because it is both a healing process as well as an experimentation process. It's a level where you learn about your likes and dislikes where food is concerned. Many people who have used this approach are often very fearful at the beginning. They worry that if they allow themselves complete freedom with food, they will totally lose control and eat an unhealthy diet for the rest of their lives. However, what I've found is that when you really start to listen to your body carefully, you may well discover that you don't want to eat pizza, bread and chocolate all day long, (the same can be said for other food groups as well). Many of the people that I have studied who have healed their relationship with food have stated that once they got a particular food 'out of their system' (psychologically speaking), they either lost interest in the food, or they started to crave a healthier choice. Strangely enough, when people tend to listen to their bodies, as opposed to following a particular diet, they usually end up naturally eating quite a balanced diet.

To illustrate this point further, I want you to imagine a dirty, cluttered room which you are going to clean. In the initial stages, the room will be in its worst state. As you begin to clean the room up, you notice just how dirty the room is, you notice the dust which has settled over the months, and as you lift away some of the clutter, you discover some dirty dishes that you had previously forgotten about. You start to move things around, experimenting with where you want things to go – sometimes liking the result, and sometimes not. You even contemplate buying new furniture. After much work, you finally see the new room emerging and you know within you that you'll never let it return to that initial stage again. However, this doesn't mean that you can't have a party – after all, you know how to clean up now ☺

The clean-up stage of this example is rather like the grey-thinking stage. You may well make mistakes; you may also find at times that you notice yourself slipping back into the black-and-white thinking, and find that you are unconsciously restricting yourself with certain foods. But as long as you can see that you are making an improvement, you're heading in the right direction. Remember that this method is not about perfection, it's about progression.

If you have had a delicate relationship with food for the most of your life, it's unlikely that it will heal immediately. Just like the dirty dishes under all the clutter in the above example, you may too find that you have some underlying issues which you may not have previously known even existed. You may also find that some of these issues are impacting other areas of your life too. However, with willingness, persistence and a commitment to learning more about yourself, you will see progress.

What I would like to add, is that although this is an experimentation stage, be very careful to be conscious of your hunger and satiety levels at all time. Yes, you will certainly be allowing yourself to explore all foods again, but it is important to keep in mind that this is not about eating what you want in whichever quantity you want, (otherwise this could turn into an endless eating session). This stage is about you re-discovering your relationship with food. It's about re-aligning yourself with your natural bodily cues, and also learning which foods work well for you and which foods don't.

The Grey Stage and Weight Loss

I would also like to remind you that weight gain is a by-product of an imbalanced relationship with both life and food. From experience, I can say that the weight will usually start to shift once you start to improve your relationship with both food and yourself.

So far, many of the people that I have worked with have started to lose weight during this stage whilst eating whatever they want and listening carefully to their hunger and satiety signals, although there hasn't been a definite pattern. Some people have lost weight quicker than others, some lost a bigger initial amount first, a few people even realised that they were already at their natural body weight, and that they had previously been striving for an unrealistic goal.

My point is that the grey stage is a healing process and everybody's journey will be different, with a lot of it being dependent on an individual's experiences and belief systems. My advice to you would be this: don't expect anything specific, rather learn from what you discover about yourself.

Stage 3 – Intuitive Response

As you start to discover more about yourself and move in line with the natural needs of your body, you move into the third stage which is the intuitive response stage. This is when you have spent time discovering and learning about both yourself and your eating habits. You have started to make choices based on how your body reacts to certain foods. You no longer rely on what others tell you to eat, but listen closely to your body and feed it accordingly. At this stage you are able to tell whether you want to eat something because your mouth wants to taste it, or because your body is truly asking for it. You may also find that you wish to learn more about nutrition. It's no longer about the weight; it's about having freedom where food is concerned, and honouring your body.

When I first started experimenting with food, I realised that eating heavy carbohydrates in the evening made me feel heavy, so I went through a phase of eating just meats and salads in the evenings (not because I had to, but because I wanted to). The only problem was that after a couple of days, I started to wake up in the middle of the night feeling sick, and I knew instantly that I needed something sweet. I then realised that perhaps my body needed more of a balance, and I was right. After some further readjustments (and re-educating myself) about my meals, I found a combination with which I was comfortable, and felt light and well most of the time.

I am also aware of certain foods now that don't sit well with my body and I choose to cut down on them. For example, I love the taste of milk chocolate, but I have noticed that I find it difficult to stop eating it once I start, it's almost addictive. I also find that I start to crave it every day if I eat it regularly. So, I have found a nice mint dark chocolate alternative which satisfies me in the same way, without the side-effects.

Before we go any further, I would like to mention one point: please be careful not to turn the Intuitive Response Model into a method that you have to follow, otherwise you could unconsciously be turning this approach into another diet, hence reverting back to black and white thinking. This is the very same trap that I fell into when I first came across intuitive eating. I just didn't realise how much a part of me the dieting mentality had actually become. I found it extremely difficult to eat whatever I wanted without feeling guilty because I had a good or bad label attached to each food. It took me a while to first legalise all foods, and then eat them only when I was hungry for them. However, it amazed me how persistent my mind was with the black-and-white thinking approach. I found that initially (with constant awareness), I was okay with eating whatever I wanted. Then after a few weeks, I would suddenly find myself unconsciously restricting my food intake in some way or another. Sometimes I would try and convince myself that I no longer craved 'unhealthy food', and other times I would catch myself saying that I'll eat whatever I want, as long as I only eat twice a day, (of course I would always be counting the calories in the back of my mind too). After a while, it became apparent to me that I was falling back into old patterns, and so, I'd release the pressure on myself and go easy on myself again. It has taken time, and consistent effort to correct my eating habits, but even now sometimes I will find myself unconsciously walking into a binge – it doesn't happen often, but when it does, I am able to stop myself half way through (sometimes).

Relationship with eating aside, you may also feel that you have a higher level of awareness about yourself and your life generally. I have had clients who in addition to healing their emotional eating have also learned to speak their truth, forgive others and take a higher level of responsibility for their own experiences. Dealing with your relationship with food opens the door to awareness and endless possibilities - if you want it.

A final reminder before concluding this section: this journey is not about perfection, it's about progression.

I AM AWARENESS

Awareness brings me strength.

I understand that every moment I have a choice. I have a choice to react or I have a choice to respond. Responding comes from a place of awareness.

I like the fact that I am more conscious of the thoughts that I choose to think.

I am grateful for the fact that life gives me a fresh new opportunity in every moment.

I am appreciative for being given freedom of thought.

I AM AWARENESS

12

STOP THE GRAMOPHONE

"Realising that you are not your thoughts is a monumental step to breaking free!"

- Sunita Pattani

There is an old gramophone in your mind that is used for frequent entertainment.

You are probably wondering why I am writing about an old gramophone and what it has to do with your mind? Well, I believe that most people, although conscious, are not choosing to live consciously. Instead they are being entertained on a daily basis by an old gramophone that in their mind just plays the same record over and over again. But the most fascinating thing is this: we have become so accustomed to hearing the music, that sometimes we believe that the music is actually part of us.

Most people have spent their entire lives thinking the same thoughts over and over, listening to the same old gramophone playing the same old record, and don't even realise what impact these thoughts are having on them.

In order to break free from emotional eating, we need to change the record. In fact, we don't even need a record all the time! What we need, is to become more conscious of the music that we are listening to and then make a choice about whether we like it or not. We need to be more aware of our thoughts and whether they are serving us the way that we want them to. The reason we find it so difficult to do this is because many of us have become 'one with our thoughts'. But our thoughts are not who we are, most of them are merely reflections of what we have been taught in the past.

Emotional Eaters and a Typical Gramophone

With regards to emotional eating, a typical gramophone may sound like this:

I woke up this morning feeling light. I knew it. I just knew it, I'd lost some more weight. I could feel the positivity building up inside me. I knew I had to weigh myself. So, I got out of bed, smiling from ear to ear, and walked over to the bathroom. I showered, I brushed my teeth. I felt good. I was thinking about all those trendy clothes that I was going to wear once I was slim. I thought about how my career was really going to take-off and do well. I wondered how I had let myself binge all these years – I must have been out of control! I was in bliss. I felt good. After I'd finished in the bathroom, I walked into my room, opened the cup-board and pulled out the bathroom scales, stepped on, knowing...feeling great, preparing myself for that half-a-pound loss (or maybe even a pound if I was lucky!)And there it was.....the pound......but it was show-ing in the wrong direction! Rather than losing a pound, I had gained a pound! I stood there in disbelief, I was absolutely sure that I had lost the weight. How on earth had I managed to put on a pound....since yester-day? My mind frantically started to search...I shouldn't have weighed myself. I promised myself that I would only weigh myself once a month (after the time of the month...when there wasn't any false PMS bloat-ing to show on the scales). It was only 8.30am. I told myself it didn't matter, that sometimes there are differences in a person's weight – it's not always accurate. I told myself that I wasn't going to beat myself up over this, I wasn't going to panic. I was going to continue eating what I wanted.

At lunch I find myself secretly counting the calories. It's ok, I am not going to panic. At 4pm, I find myself telling myself that I should just let go for today. Tomorrow is a new day. I can start again from tomorrow, and I won't be weighing myself...I didn't eat properly at lunch anyway. I can see myself persuading myself, giving into that voice in my head – the gramophone. I know what I am doing, but I don't want to be doing it. But frankly, the only thing I can think about is the chip shop. I gained a bloody pound!

It's evening now, I feel physically sick laying in bed...the chips stopped tasting good half way through the meal, but I didn't stop eating. I gained a bloody pound! – Or maybe two by now.

This was one of my journal extracts. That day, my whole day had been consumed with the pound that I had gained. Looking at the number on the scales I started to panic and my mind started doing overtime having me count calories and then eventually bingeing. I had fallen into my old patterns again. Had I chosen not to weigh myself that morning, I would have carried on feeling fantastic the whole day, and I would have continued to eat in the 'food is food and emotions are emotions' way.

Instead, that whole day I listened to the gramophone which seemed to get louder by the hour and occasionally I would jump into the future, imaging the worst - me, the size of Planet Earth. I had forgotten that the only moment in which I could make a difference was now. I had forgotten to live in the present moment.

How often do you actually spend experiencing the present moment? You'll probably find that when you start thinking of diets or overeating, the gramophone has started to play and your mind is playing out an old pattern. This music then tricks you into thinking that by eating in a certain way, you'll be okay.

However in reality, that gramophone in your head is stopping you from following your intuition and moving towards a more balanced approach in thinking. That music is the cause of you giving away your power and responsibility. When you start to notice the thought, (whether it's an urge to overeat, under eat, or an urge to diet), and acknowledge that it is the result of a past belief system, you automatically start to detach yourself from it. This means that it is no longer a part of your present situation, it's only an illusion. And when you understand this, you begin to realise that you have a choice in each moment, you have a choice of whether you want to overeat, or whether you want to subject yourself to food restrictions. The fact of the matter is that when you are able to isolate your eating from the sound of the gramophone, you are able to live in the present moment, and you will most probably start to lose weight because you are eating for the correct reasons, in the quantity that is right for you.

Many people also become trapped in the illusion that their life will be wonderful when they lose all the weight, that all of a sudden they won't have any more challenges, and that they will win over love and acceptance from everyone. But this too is a false belief that we have. (Perhaps it comes from the advertising world, where the television commercials imply that your life will improve once you have purchased a certain product?)

Whilst it is true that once you've lost the weight you'll probably be able to move better and wear a wider variety of clothing, it's important to realise that you will still be you, with all the same issues in your life as before. If you have been slim before, you need to ask yourself whether it brought you true happiness, and kept you in shape? If it didn't bring you the happiness that you thought it would, what makes you think it will this time? It's more than likely that the gramophone in your head is making you false promises again.

By staying in the present moment you become aware that this is your life right now. Right now you have the option to listen to your body and to do all the things that you believe you'll do once you reach your natural blueprint weight. The more you begin to practice staying in the present moment, the more choices you'll have available to you. Your life is waiting to be lived now.

PUTTING IT INTO PRACTICE

1. You may find it helpful to turn the negative thoughts or self-talk into a humorous character as this may make it easier for you to dismiss the voice. Mine for example, is a 1 ft. Clown with black curly hair, and when he speaks it reminds me of how ridiculous his suggestions are.

2. Get used to the idea of observing your thoughts. Just spend some time watching what you think. When you start to do this, you will soon realise that many of the thoughts are pointless and of an absurd nature. It's worth questioning what makes the thought of dieting or overeating so believable – after all, they too are just mere thoughts brought about by your past-programming. Start to recognise them for what they are, and you will start to free yourself from the prison of food.

What to Expect

I remember clearly the first few weeks of my journey. There seemed to be no sign of the binge at all and I honestly thought that I had cracked the formula. Then, after a few weeks, it happened. I don't know where the urge came from, but within minutes I had decided that I wanted to eat, and eat and eat and eat. Anyway, it took me a few days to work out what was going on and I realised that the reason behind the binge was emotional. I dealt with it, and resumed my intuitive eating pattern again.

However, a few weeks later, I felt the urge to binge again, and there seemed to be no apparent reason for the onset. I couldn't understand what was going on, until I realised that the gramophone, the 'voice in my head' had started to rebel. My old-programming was trying to stop me from moving out of my comfort zone.

When you start to form new belief systems, it's important to realise that sometimes your old-programming may try to keep you trapped in your comfort zone. Think back to when we used the stickperson analogy to demonstrate how the mind works. If your mind has been used to receiving certain ideas about eating, it will have formed a habit. When you now try to introduce a new way of eating, your mind may protest because that's not what it is used to.

Whenever you feel like you are slipping into old belief patterns, take out a few minutes to just stop and focus on you. (If you find social gatherings difficult and know that they could act as a trigger, use the bathroom to get away for a few minutes). Take a few deep breaths, and then bring your attention to your stomach. How does it feel? How hungry are you? What do you feel like eating? Remember you know just how much food your body actually needs, so just take this time to really tune in to your physical hunger level. Next bring your attention to your emotions. How are you feeling? Do you feel calm or overwhelmed? What do you think is causing these feelings to come up? Perhaps there aren't any direct emotions that you can feel, and you just feel like eating. Think of your mouth for a moment, what is it that your mouth wants to eat? Is it the same as your body is asking for?

Focusing on the present moment will really help you to realign with yourself. I know a lot of clients of mine who find social gatherings or festive holidays difficult (due to the fact that there is so much food around), use this technique frequently. When you give yourself some time and choose to focus on the present moment, you are giving yourself a chance to decide upon your next step.

Aside from practicing 'being present' whilst you are eating, it is also useful to practice similar techniques in your daily life. Ancient Buddhists and Hindus used the process of mediation to tame 'uncontrollable thinking' and reduce negative thoughts and actions. Mediation also has a calming influence on the body and mind, helping to reduce anxiety and enabling you to stay conscious of your emotions and emotional patterns. Try taking some time out on a daily basis, (even if it's just for ten minutes), to sit in silence and focus on your breathing, noticing each inward and outward breath. If you have trouble relaxing, please get in touch, as I may be able to help you.

I AM ABUNDANCE

It feels good to be reminded that I already have a natural guiding system within which shows me the way.

By reconnecting with my authentic self, I open the door to abundant opportunity.

I like the thought that 'wellness is my natural state.'

There is always support available for me.

I am surrounded by people and circumstances that support my wellbeing.

I deserve abundance in all form.

I AM ABUNDANCE

13

OPENING THE DOOR TO FREEDOM

"The journey of a thousand miles starts with a single step."

- Lao Tzu

Well, we are nearly at the end of the book and I have told you everything that I know about emotional eating. This chapter is all about you moving forward and setting the foundation to set yourself free. I have started this chapter by summarising the main principles outlined in this book which I consider to be essential to your progress.

1. Different people will experience emotional eating in varying degrees.

    There will be some people that will find that they resonate with *most* of what I have written in this book, and there will also be a few individuals that will resonate with *some* of what I have shared with you. For example, someone who eats unconsciously may well be able to correct their behaviour just by becoming aware of responding to their hunger-satiety signals. But there will be some people who have struggled long and hard with emotional eating for much of their life, and so their journey will look very different.

    The fact of the matter is that everyone experiences emotional eating in different ways and I would urge you keep this factor in mind. This is **your journey**. The way in which you experience it will be unique to you, so don't compare your progress to anyone else's.

2. Assume 100% responsibility for your actions. Know that you are in charge of what you manifest. Commit to listening to your body and changing your belief system.

3. Keep in mind The *Foundation* at all times: consider yourself to be a 'whole', your natural state is one of well-being, and your need to eat is really a calling that you need to find out what's going on within.

4. Stay well connected to your body's physical hunger-satiety signals.

5. Learn to identify the difference between physical and emotional hunger.

6. Practice conscious eating. This will not only help you to become more aligned with the way that your body is feeling, but it will also help you to establish whether you actually like the taste of what you are eating. Remember to explore different foods whilst noticing the effects that they have on your body.

7. Start to acknowledge the power of your mind and emotions.

8. Watch out for black and white thinking.

9. Find ways of dealing with your emotional discomfort.

10. Take your time with this journey and have some fun along the way! If you find that you are the type of person that eats when you get happy, then learn to become more conscious of the choices that you are making. Many people eat when they are surrounded by family or are at a party because they have always equated food with these experiences in the past. The thing to always keep in mind is this: if your body isn't physically hungry, it's not ready for digestion.

Where Are You?

At the beginning of the book I asked you where you were with regards to your eating. But I am going to conclude this book by asking you where you are in terms of your thinking. In other words where is your mind set?

In order to start to replace your negative patterns, it is important to know where you are at. In chapter 11, we looked the Intuitive Response Model. The diagram below builds upon that concept by sharing with you different levels along that journey. This will give you a clear picture of where you are and where you wish to be heading.

The Awareness Pyramid

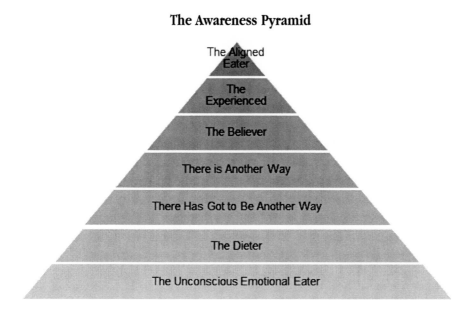

The Aligned Eater

The Experienced

The Believer

There is Another Way

There Has Got to Be Another Way

The Dieter

The Unconscious Emotional Eater

The Unconscious Emotional Eater

This is the level where you operate from a **reactive perspective**. Many people are stuck at this point without even realising that they are here. At this level, you react blindly to something without thinking about the consequences properly.

For example, many of us have been in a place where someone has made a nasty comment about our weight and it's really upset us, perhaps even pushing us to overeat. At this stage we give away our personal power and allow external circumstances to dictate our reaction. We would rather blame someone for where we are, rather than take responsibility for ourselves.

People at this stage may continue eating excessively (even if they know that it's detrimental to their health), than face up to healing themselves. Some people will not even be aware that your body is capable of communicating with you. At this stage, there would be no concept of balance; hence you would be stuck in the black-and-white thinking stage.

The Dieter

This is the next level up from the unconscious. At this stage, people want to make a change. They no longer want to be overweight, and are willing to take some responsibility for their actions, which is a fantastic sign.

Having stepped out of the unconscious stage, the most obvious thing to do would be to look at how most people are approaching the challenge, and do the same. Most if the time, this means going on a diet of some sort, or joining a weight loss club. Although it's great that a person is willing to take responsibility for themselves at this stage, they still allow others to tell them what is best for them. (Please note that an obvious exception would be a medical condition.) They learn to trust others rather than themselves. Usually, they become familiar with what they should and shouldn't eat and therefore, strengthen their black-and-white thinking. They may lose the weight in the short-term, but in the long term, many of them are setting themselves up for an uphill struggle.

There Has Got to Be Another Way

Many people reading this may well be at this stage. Although we are climbing up the pyramid, and we should be making progress at each level, if you don't manage to shift from this level, you could remain stuck between this stage and its predecessor.

At this stage, you realise that dieting, following rules and measuring food are becoming cumbersome for you. You are finding it increasingly difficult to uphold your diets, and frequently find yourself 'falling off the wagon'. It is likely that you find socialising a chore as everything revolves around making sure you don't overeat. Many people may even give up diets at this point and decide to accept that they will never be naturally thin, so they may as well eat whatever they want.

Most people at this point however, will still have an aspiration to be in good shape, but they simply cannot adhere to their strict belief systems where food is concerned, and are constantly hunting for the new diet in town that will either allow them to eat a little bit more, or promises to make them slim easily and quickly.

At this level, black-and-white thinking is still ruling your life, and by reinforcing it each day, you're making it harder for yourself to be at peace with food.

There is Another Way

Some of you reading this may be at this level. At this stage you begin to question and seriously believe that there is another way to obtain your natural blueprint shape. You simply cannot continue the dieting anymore and you start to research alternative methods of reaching your ideal weight. Many people at this point will try different therapies such as hypnotherapy, counselling, or perhaps some self-image work. They may even begin to discover the intuitive eating process, and start to work with some of the principles outlined in this book.

This stage is really when you begin to discover that change comes from within and you begin to step out of black-and-white thinking and enter the grey stage of thinking. You're willing to make mistakes and forgive yourself for doing so.

The problem with the previous level is that your old subconscious programming still takes over a majority of the time, and you fall into the same old pattern of overeating and going back on diets.

When you reach this level however, you actually become more aware that a lot of the time you are operating from past programming. You begin to actively take the step to move forward and are aware that you are doing so, and if you continue to do so, you will reach the fifth level, the *Believer*.

The Believer

This is really where you start to act on your new decision continuously, where you become 'disciplined', where you start to practice your commitment. You start to listen carefully to your body and honour it. You also don't beat yourself up if you slip up or overeat.

Eventually this becomes a way of life and your natural blueprint shape will start to emerge. I'd like to point out that it takes around thirty days to start to form a new habit. In fact, when I seriously decided to change and tackle my binge eating, I was surprised that after around thirty days, the overeating seemed like a distant memory. (I still had certain challenges and sometimes I still do, but I could see that a new healthier pattern of eating was emerging.) Once you apply commitment and continue to believe and practice whatever you are doing, the gap between what you 'know' and what you 'do' begins to close.

The Experienced

This is the difference between 'knowing' and 'doing'. When I had serious eating issues, I was consulting many experts in the field and obtaining contradictory opinions. When I started to embark upon this journey I realised that the only person that knew what was best for me was me. This was because I was the only person who knew how I reacted to certain foods. I also gave myself permission to be gentle with myself, something that some experts didn't have room for.

The reason this concept works so well, and why my clients make such good progress is because I have been there. I have been where you are, and although our issues may not be the same, I can certainly understand the feelings that you must be experiencing. This is your journey and you will only know what works for you when you've experienced it – everyone is different. For example, one of my clients was telling me that when she was at her lowest ebb, people would continually tell her that she was wasting her years away, and that she should dress up well anyway because it would make her feel better. She told me that although she knew that she would look better, she disagreed that it would make her feel better. This was because she had some deeper issues relating to her sexuality. She had never been brought up to appreciate her body, so she felt really uncomfortable dressing up. For her, hiding behind baggy clothes was protection, ensuring that she did not have to confront those issues. It wasn't that she didn't want to look nice, but she had to deal with a few issues first. Once she started to work on herself and her eating issues, gradually she was able to dress differently.

What I am trying to illustrate here is that most people wouldn't have understood how she felt from the outset, only she knew deep down how (and whether) she wanted to tackle her issues.

The other great change that comes with experience is that you begin to see which foods settle with you and which foods don't. You become more aware of this, and you may find that you start to make healthier choices automatically. You'll also find that you experience more pleasure where food is concerned, and you'll start to trust that you can lose weight and maintain your natural body weight without depriving yourself in anyway. At this level your thinking will have shifted from the grey stage to the intuitive response stage for most of the time.

The Aligned Eater

This is when you have mastered your relationship with food and continue to live the intuitive response stage. Does it mean that it will be perfect from here on? Not necessarily, you may still struggle with certain emotional issues or you may still find special occasions a bit of a challenge. But, most of the time you will be tuned into your body and the way it feels. At this point you will probably be at your natural body weight, and very relaxed around food.

There is No 'Right Way' or 'One Solution'

One of the hardest things when it comes to breaking the dieting mentality is that there is no longer any structure to follow. You are left with the option to learn to trust yourself and develop a relationship with food and your body that firstly works in rhythm with you and secondly, favours your health.

You see, when you think that there is a 'right' way of doing things, then naturally there is also a 'wrong' way of doing things. Therefore you remain trapped in the illusion of black-and-white thinking.

Trusting yourself is probably one of the most daunting tasks that you'll ever undertake because most of us from a very young age are taught otherwise. We are taught to trust what everyone else says because we believe that we don't know what is best for us. And whilst it is true that there are many experts whose help and knowledge we greatly appreciate, we have to come to terms with the fact that we do have some knowledge about what is right for our bodies. This isn't necessarily what we 'think' is right for us, it's more about what we 'feel' is right for us. In order to develop a trusting relationship with our bodies, we are required to really listen to what it is trying to communicate to us.

There are some key questions that we can ask ourselves to ascertain whether we are moving in the right direction, and whether our actions are causing us to lead more of a fulfilling life. Is the food that you consume causing you to feel good? Are you engaged in a practice where you are learning to trust yourself and your internal wisdom? Do your choices empower and strengthen you? It's also worth considering that we live in a universe where nothing is ever stationary. Everything is in a constant state of change. As you evolve and grow, so will your choices. What you felt may have been right for you during one point of your life, may not be appropriate for you now.

There is no 'right' way to do things. You have a beautiful body which will guide you if you let it. The likelihood is that the more you begin to love, respect and trust your body, the more empowering choices you will make regarding your food and health. When one of my clients was asked whether she felt the need to overeat anymore, she replied, "*it took a while, but now I just can't abuse my body anymore. I am worth so much more than that.*" So be curious about yourself. What messages is your body sending you? And are you listening well? Experiment with different foods and learn what works well with your body and what doesn't. Nobody is going to come and give you a magic pill or cure because there isn't one. No matter how small you start, it's a step in the right direction. In the famous words of a famous philosopher: "*the journey of a thousand miles starts with a single step.*"

I AM LOVE

"I owe it to myself to look after myself. I have a right to health. I have a right to choosing foods that feel good in my body. I have a right to stop obsessing about my weight and about the way in which I eat, because I know when I 'eat right' for me, my body feels better.

I have a body which deserves the best nutrition possible for me and I know that my natural body shape will emerge. I trust in the power of my life force to lovingly guide me.

I deserve the best on this brief journey that we call life.

I AM the creator of my own experience.

I AM love."

EPILOGUE

My journey with food has taken me from the secretive, guilty lover of all food forbidden, to someone who still loves food, but has regained her love and respect for herself and has stopped damaging her health and relationships. The path to finding this is not an easy one when you have to step off the well trodden road you have always taken, but it is essential to explore your own feelings and show yourself some love as you begin to address the real issues that lie within.

Perhaps the most shocking revelation for me has been that my relationship with food has actually been a very powerful opening into self-discovery. A topic that is often explored solely on a physical and psychological level, is in my opinion at its core, one of a spiritual nature, and unless explored to its depth runs the risk of remaining unhealed.

One of the challenges that I have faced along my journey has been the lack of support and awareness available on emotional eating. For years I compared myself to others, trying desperately to mould myself into their model of eating, and all the while becoming further and further drawn into the abyss of emotional eating until eventually developing binge eating disorder. What I realized from my own journey was that binge eating disorder was not something that I developed all of a sudden, but rather it was a gradual onset that worsened over time. As I began to offer tools to people to help heal themselves, I realised just how different everyone's experiences were and that's when I started to understand the importance of awareness. Emotional eating wasn't as straight forward as I had thought – the range was wide, and people often sought help when they felt that the issue had gotten out of hand. Yes, there was some good support available for those who suffered from eating disorders, but what about those individuals that couldn't be considered in the category of eating disorders? What about the pain that I was witnessing in individuals who felt terrible about the shapes of their body on a daily basis? I couldn't help but think what the outcome would have been for me had I have been introduced to the concept of emotional eating and how to heal myself before things got out of hand.

Today as I write this epilogue, I am in the process of setting up *The Feel Free Project*, to help promote awareness and to offer tools to prevent and heal emotional eating. This project isn't just about helping those who are experiencing the deeper end of emotional eating, but it's also about helping to educate those who are engaging in milder forms of emotional eating. My vision is to see people freeing themselves from emotional eating and to give themselves freedom around food whilst getting in touch with their inner wisdom. I feel there's good hope that if people have a greater awareness about this topic, then prevention and healing may become easier.

So, for those that have ever experienced any level of emotional eating, be it an innocent attempt at food control, or be it finding yourself in a constant cycle of bingeing and dieting, begin your journey. Begin your journey, make mistakes and learn from them. Learn to love life, and yourself, again.

I wish you all the best in finding your happiness and inner peace,

Until we meet,

Sunita.

www.thefeelfreeproject.com

FREQUENTLY ASKED QUESTIONS

You say that we can eat whatever we want, but isn't that just really unhealthy?

Giving yourself permission to eat whatever you want does not translate into, "*I can eat whatever I want, whenever I want, without taking into consideration the way that my body feels*". This approach is all about taking into consideration how your body feels once you have consumed a particular food and then taking responsibility to nourish yourself appropriately.

The other thing to consider is that if you have been stuck in a binge-diet cycle, then realistically you may already be eating all the foods that you perceive to be unhealthy in large quantities anyway. I am asking you to become conscious of what you are doing and how well these decisions suit your body. It makes sense to engage in 'conscious experimenting' where eating is concerned so that you are able to realign with your natural body signals again. Yes, it may take a bit of time, but it is it is definitely healthier than the binge-starving cycle.

It's also worth considering that nutritional science is important because ultimately what you eat matters. Therefore, I would recommend that you start to experiment with different fresh, natural, healthy foods. The idea however, is **not** to turn this into a diet, but rather use the information and experience to become an expert on yourself. Also please remember to check out the Feel Free Project website frequently (www.thefeelfreeproject.com), as we are aiming to provide both classes and information on nutritional science in the near future.

Do you have any suggestions as to what I can do to help myself in the middle of a binge?

The first thing that I will say about a binge is that they are signals. They are signals that something inside of you is not quite right. At some level you are depriving yourself of some essential self-care. At the moment that you experience the need to binge, you are choosing to numb out, you are choosing not to tune into what is really going on.

For some of you the binges will be hours long and, for others, a-bag-of-chips long. Ultimately it doesn't matter how long the binge is. What matters is that 'I-want-it-now feeling' and how you choose to deal with it. The thing is, many of us just need a break, some 'me time' when this urge comes on, and because it isn't always socially acceptable to take a break, we choose to eat instead.

So, one of the things that I would suggest is to do something everyday which brings you pleasure. Remember, one of our *foundations* is that our need to overeat is a sign that we need to reconnect with the joy of life again. So make it a priority that each day you do something that will make you feel good.

As this is a journey about progression and not perfection, you will most likely experience some bingeing episodes still, and you may want to try the following strategies:

- **Stop and breathe**. Allowing yourself time to stop, breathe and relax brings your awareness back to you. This time and space will allow you to decide what you want to do next.

- **Allow yourself to finish the act of bingeing**. Yes, you heard correctly because when you give yourself permission openly and honestly, you allow yourself to become more conscious of the choices that you are making. You allow yourself to *show up for your mealtimes*. As long as you are focussing on the thoughts that you are 'doing something wrong' by bingeing, you are engaging in negative thoughts about yourself, and because these thoughts don't feel good, you continue the act of mindless eating. Start to become aware of what you're doing. And if you decide to continue the binge, at least give yourself permission to enjoy the food.

- **Talk to yourself.** In the early days, when I used to get the urge to binge, I made it a habit to talk to myself about what was happening and reason with myself what the pros and cons would be. I would tell myself that it was my decision and that I could go ahead and binge if I wanted to. For some reason, this process helped me to reflect on what was going on within. It helped bring to light the gramophone that was playing in my mind again. I always had two choices: listen to the gramophone, or choose a different action.

- **Forgive yourself afterwards and shower yourself with kindness.**

This is a crucial step. If you abandon yourself at this point, you will only end up feeling negative about yourself, and hence are leaving yourself open to a binge again. Therefore do whatever it takes to be kind to yourself. Acknowledge the fact that the bingeing session is now in the past, and it's time to move on and focus on the 'now'.

Another piece of valuable advice: eat when you next get hungry. Don't deprive yourself of food just because you feel guilty about the earlier binge. Be mindful of black-and-white thinking and avoid the binge-starve cycle. Continue to trust your body.

- **Be inquisitive about the binge. What did it teach you about yourself, what did you learn from it?**

Remember that there is a very good reason for why you choose to over-eat in the first place. Take some time out to reflect upon your actions. How were you feeling before you decided to binge? How could you take better care of yourself next time, so that you don't end up turning to food?

I have heard that you should not label foods 'good' or 'bad', but surely some foods are better for you than other foods?

I am not keen on using the terms 'good' and 'bad' because as they may provoke a 'guilty' feeling within individuals. I prefer instead to acknowledge that there are foods of different nutritional value. Remember your aim is not to force change by blaming or beating yourselves up, but rather to initiate change in a loving manner.

I think ultimately, when it comes down to it, we all have an idea of what the nutritionally rich foods are. But here's the thing: we knew about these nutritionally rich foods when we were engaging in diets as well, and yet we still found the diets difficult to adhere to. You see, as you start to really honour and respect yourself, you'll find that your perception of food changes. It is no longer a case of forcing or moulding yourself into shape, but rather a case of *wanting* to take care of your body. Imagine being in a place, where you felt such love for your physical body, that you wouldn't put anything into it which would impair its optimum function in any way.

I don't think that the human body was designed to function entirely on pizza and cake. If you give yourself a chance to understand the emotional links that you have with food and then work on healing them, you will find that your body will begin to crave the nutritionally rich foods too. Again, our natural state I believe, is one of well-being.

How long will this whole process take, how long will it take me to shift the weight?

I know that this might be difficult for some people to do, but I would suggest that you take the focus off the weight for a while and focus on health and *becoming an expert on yourself* instead. As mentioned in a previous chapter (and excluding medical conditions), weight gain is often a symptom, with the cause being of an emotional nature. Once you start to address the cause as well as starting to listen to your body, you will find that your weight will begin to normalise. However, as this is a common question, I have still provided the answer in the following paragraphs:

Everybody is different. I have known people that have started to lose weight in a very short period of time, whereas others have taken longer. Some people have even come to realise that they are at their natural shape and have to work on accepting it. It all depends on what you've previously experienced and also your level of commitment.

I have had some clients who have underestimated the level of commitment that was required. I have also had a few clients who think that they are ready for the change, but really they're not. They're not quite willing to face up to their emotions or to get conscious about what they are eating. These people still choose to use food as their companion or support in life, and really it's their choice.

So ask yourself how committed you are to becoming an expert on yourself. If you commit to doing your part, I am sure your body will reciprocate and re-align itself. As ironic as it sounds, I would ask you to consider taking your mind off the weight-loss, and focus instead on action and foods that makes your body feel good. The rest will take care of itself.

What makes this system so different from rest?

This system is different because it gives you the tools to make permanent changes in the way that you relate to food, your body and your weight. The principles outlined in this book are designed to empower you and help you to realise that you have the power and wisdom already within you.

I would also say that the primary foundation of this philosophy is based on love, not fear – which is the foundation that most diets are based on. One of my strongest beliefs is that nobody ever made amazing progress by hating themselves. I believe that if you've come this far into reading this book, your previous attempts at weight loss or improved self-image haven't worked. It's time to try something different.

I have read the book, but am finding it difficult to apply the principles. Is there any more help available?

Yes. In fact, most of the people that I have worked with have required extra support, and the reason for this is that people are often working to change long-held belief systems, hence they find the extra support extremely beneficial.

We offer a number of workshops each month, where the concepts presented in this book are explored in more detail. These workshops are an excellent opportunity for meeting like-minded people and asking lots of questions. We only take on a small number of participants on each workshop so that everyone has a chance to get actively involved. A mentioned in the epilogue, I am also in the process of setting up *The Feel Free Project* which aims to promote awareness and solutions to tackling emotional eating. We aim to offer a number of services including personal sessions, workshops and nutritional science education. Please visit www.thefeelfreeproject.com for more information.

Is it ok to weigh myself?

The point of this concept is that you learn to trust to your own judgement about yourself. I guess the question I would ask you is this: what is your primary intention for weighing yourself? If the answer is to see whether you have lost any weight, then I would ask you another question: what if you haven't lost any weight? How will this affect your mood? Will you be angry at yourself for not losing weight? Will you contemplate turning to another diet – knowing the long-term consequences? If the answer to these questions is yes, then you need to ask yourself what purpose the scales are serving. The fact of the matter is that the number on the scales doesn't define who you are as a person. The thing to remember is to go with how your body feels. You will know that you are losing weight because your clothes will fit better and you'll feel better within yourself.

Having said that, because this system is all about self-trust, I will leave the decision up to you. If you feel that weighing yourself may be of benefit to you, then go ahead and weigh yourself. But, as a word of caution, I wouldn't advise you to weigh yourself frequently as body weight can fluctuate considerably according to a variety of factors.

BIBLIOGRAPHY

Chopra, D. (1994) Perfect Weight. Three Rivers Press, USA. p.10

McTaggart, L. (2003) The Field. Harper Collins Publishers, UK. Reprinted by permission of HarperCollins Publishers Ltd © 2003 (Lynn McTaggart)

Ogden, J. (2005) The Psychology of Eating: From Healthy to Disordered Behaviour. Wiley-Blackwell Publishers, UK. p.125

Orbach, S. (2002) On Eating: Change Your Eating, Change Your Life. Penguin Publishers, UK. p.68

Wansink, B. (2009) Mindless Eating – Why We Eat More Than We Think. Hay House Publishers, UK. p.25

Welwood, J. (1998) Love and Awakening: Discovering the Sacred Path of Intimate Relationship. Harper Collins, USA. pp.10-13. Reprinted by permission of HarperCollins Publishers © 1996 (John Welwood).

FURTHER READING

Braden, G. (2007) The Spontaneous Healing of Belief: Shattering the Paradigm of False Limits. Hay House Publishers.

Cooper, D. (2004) A Little Light on Spiritual Laws. Mobius Publishers.

Dyer, W. (2007) Change Your Thoughts, Change Your Life – The Wisdom of the Tao. Hay House Publishers, USA.

Gauding, M. (2005) Meditation Bible: A Definitive Guide to Meditation for Every Purpose. Godfield Press Ltd. UK.

Maltz, M. (2007) The New Psychocybernetics. The Original Science of Self-Improvement and Success that Has Changed the Lives of 30 Million People. Souvenir Press, UK.

Murphy, J. (2008) The Power of Your Subconscious Mind: Unlock Your Master Key to Success. Thornton Wilder Publishers, USA.

Roth, G. (2003) Breaking Free From Emotional Eating. Simon & Schuster Publishers, USA.

Tolle, E. (2005) The Power of Now: A Guide to Spiritual Enlightenment. Hodder & Mobius, UK.

More from J Publishing Company Ltd.

The Pariah Goddess
By Smita Singh

What is common between a pulverized woman and global warming? Amira fancies that the moment she arrived on the land of the Queen, she was recruited as a private into the troop headed by Staff Sergeant Khan.

K is an urban Londoner devoted to her job at Go Green. She loves life and lives by her own rules. One of her rules is 'give back as good as you get' and another one is 'life is a game so play it.' No one knows what her game plan is, not even her best friend Ian.

Mouth Full
By Sweta Srivastava Vikram

Mouth full is a collection of person essays chronicling the emotional journey of modern-day immigrants as they move to a new country, assimilate in the culture, and learn a different way of life. Somewhere in all of that movement, the experiences teach them to see the strengths and weaknesses of both the homeland and acquired land. It also raises concern about the socio-cultural issues and racial expectations in the two nations. Told from the perspective of a modern day Indian immigrant as social questions, observations, and commentary, the essays are funny, bold, sassy, and uninhibited.

Visit us at: www.jpublishingcompany.co.uk